THE

DOUBLE

PLANET

by ISAAC ASIMOV

Illustrations by John Bradford

ABELARD-SCHUMAN
London   New York   Toronto

Abelard-Schuman Books
by ISAAC ASIMOV

The Chemicals of Life

Races and People
[WITH WILLIAM C. BOYD]

Inside the Atom

Building Blocks of the Universe

Only a Trillion

The World of Carbon

The World of Nitrogen

The Clock We Live On

The Kingdom of the Sun

The Double Planet

London
Abelard-Schuman
Limited
8 King Street

New York
Abelard-Schuman
Limited
6 West 57th Street

Toronto
Abelard-Schuman
Canada Limited
81 John Street

Printed in the United States of America

5694

To LEW SCHWARTZ,
who has treated me well.

CONTENTS

1. A Sphere 13

2. Not Quite a Sphere 25

3. The Layers Beneath 41

4. Outside the Crust 53

5. Outside the Air 66

6. The Nearness of "Nearest" 77

7. The Circlings of the Worlds 88

8. We Are Pulled 99

9. We Pull Back 109

10. Airlessness 120

   Appendix One: Some Facts About the Earth 139

   Appendix Two: Some Facts About the Moon 143

   Appendix Three: A Table of Dates 146

   Index 151

ILLUSTRATIONS

The Disappearing Hull   15

The Disappearing Stars   17

Rotation at Different Speeds   30

An Oblate Spheroid   31

Divisions of the Circle   36

Measuring the Mass of the Earth   43

Internal Structure of the Earth   49

The Thickness of the Crust   51

The Barometer   56

Layers of the Atmosphere   63

The Earth As a Magnet   69

Magnetic Lines of Force   70

The Van Allen Radiation Belts   75

Angles and Distances   80

Parallax and Distance   84

The Earth and the Moon Compared   86

Ellipses   92

The Moon's Orbit   94

The Center of Gravity   97

The Procession of the Equinoxes   107

The Rotation of the Moon   112

Escape Velocity   125

THE DOUBLE PLANET

ONE

A SPHERE

In Florida, in California, in certain places in the Soviet Union, rockets point upward. Some have been fired into space and made to take up orbits around our planet. Others have been fired past the moon and have become tiny planets themselves, circling the sun.

These rockets are gateways to new knowledge and to other worlds.

Already most of us are looking forward confidently to the time when human beings will be carried by such rockets to the moon. Almost surely, this will happen before very many years have passed.

When this happens, it will be our first step across space; and it will be a short one. The moon is closer to Earth than is any other heavenly body. The two travel through space together, and each is separated by many millions of miles from any other world. It may be many years after the first landing on the moon before mankind can reach out still farther.

And yet there will be much to find out about the moon. Scientists will be kept busy for a long time.

As a matter of fact, an important result of the sending up of rockets and satellites so far is to add greatly to our knowledge of our own world—the earth. You mustn't think that because we are reaching for other worlds, we know all about our own planet. Mankind has been seeking for knowledge of the earth for thousands of years, but the search still continues. It is by no means over. It will probably never be over.

This book is the story of some of the things man has discovered and is discovering about the earth, and about the nearest other target of human curiosity, the moon.

The Surface Curves

People in the dim, dim past must have wondered about the earth, and perhaps the first thing they wondered about was whether it came to an end somewhere. It might naturally seem that there must be an end, because everything has an end.

Furthermore, it would seem that although the earth might rise up occasionally in bumps and hills, it was generally flat. After all, if it weren't flat, people would fall off, or at least go slipping and sliding down a slope. Besides, in lowlands, and on the sea especially, you could see with your own eyes that the earth was flat.

The earliest maps of the Greeks, for instance, showed a flat earth with an end to it. On such a map, Greece would be in the center, naturally. The Mediterranean Ocean was drawn in, along with the lands that bordered it: southern Europe, northern Africa, western Asia. Greek travelers had visited all these lands and reported on them. Around all this known part of the world was a circular river called Okeanos. (From that river we get our word "ocean.") Okeanos was the circling rim of the world; it was the end; there was nothing beyond it.

To the Greeks of about 600 B. C., then, the world was shaped like a flat disk, a large dinner plate, perhaps four thousand miles across.

And yet it was the sea that first must have spoiled the pretty notion of the flat earth; the very sea that looked so flat. The Greeks were a seafaring people and a very curious-about-everything sort of people. Some of them must have become aware of a curious thing—that a ship grew smaller and disappeared as it sailed out to sea.

Keen eyes noticed that when a ship was quite a distance away, but still well within sight, only its top parts were visible. The hull of the ship was hidden as though it had sunk beneath the surface of the water.

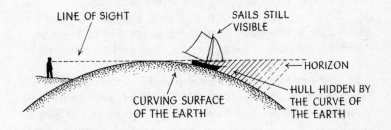

LINE OF SIGHT

SAILS STILL VISIBLE

HORIZON

CURVING SURFACE OF THE EARTH

HULL HIDDEN BY THE CURVE OF THE EARTH

The Disappearing Hull

Of course, the ship hadn't sunk beneath the water. When the sailors returned they could bear witness to that. Another explanation, then, was that the ship was sailing down the side of a very gently sloping hill. If you were watching a person walk over the crest of a hill and down the other side, you would see his legs pass out of view first, then his chest, then his head.

Could that be happening to the ship? Could the sea be a hill, even though it looked flat?

Furthermore, this trick of disappearing bottom first happened to ships in every port in about the same way. Nor did it matter in which direction the ship was traveling. This made it seem as though the sea were a hill that curved equally in all directions and in all places.

An object that curves equally in all directions and in all places is a *sphere*. So, in ancient Greek times, a few men began to suggest that the earth was not flat, but was a sphere.

The first men supposed to have suggested this were Pythagoras of Samos, who lived about 525 B. C., and his followers. They pictured the earth as a sphere suspended in space and surrounded by the much larger sphere of the sky. Their reasons for this, however, did not depend on observation but on philosophical arguments. For instance, they felt that the spherical shape was the most perfect, so naturally the earth would be a sphere.

By 350 B.C. the spherical shape of the earth was accepted by most Greek thinkers, and observation of nature was used to support the idea. The great philosopher Aristotle of Stagira listed several of these observations. Two of them involved the heavens.

For instance, the earth occasionally passes between the sun and the moon. When this happens, the moon's light (which is only the reflection of sunlight) is dimmed. The moon, in other words, passes into the earth's shadow and this is called a *lunar eclipse*. As the earth's shadow passes across the moon, little by little, the shadow can be clearly seen to have a circular shape. Aristotle pointed out that a sphere would cast a circular shadow.

Of course, a flat round disk could also cast a circular shadow. However, if the earth were flat, Aristotle pointed out, the various stars in heaven ought to be visible to all parts of the earth when they shone in the night sky. If the stars were close to Earth, their positions might change as one moved about on Earth, but they would stay visible.

If the earth were spherical, however, a star might be

visible at one point of the earth and not at another. The "hump" of the sphere would get in the way of the line of vision.

Sure enough, travelers reported that as they traveled north, for instance, certain stars disappeared beyond the southern horizon. So the earth couldn't be flat. And what with the circular shadow on the moon, and the sea being an equal hill in all directions, the earth just had to be spherical.

All this must have been difficult for ordinary people to accept, because it seemed to go against "common sense."

The Disappearing Stars

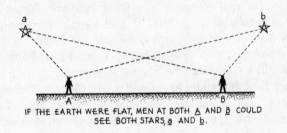

IF THE EARTH WERE FLAT, MEN AT BOTH A AND B COULD SEE BOTH STARS, a AND b.

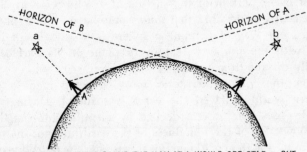

IF THE EARTH WERE ROUND, THE MAN AT A WOULD SEE STAR a, BUT STAR b WOULD BE BELOW HIS HORIZON · THE MAN AT B WOULD SIMILARLY SEE STAR b, BUT NOT STAR a.

Talk about disappearing stars and shadows on the moon and ships sailing downhill might be all right for philosophers, but it all must have seemed impossible to other people. If the oceans curved downhill, why didn't all the water run off? If the earth was a sphere, why didn't everything seem to tip as one traveled from Greece to Spain, for instance?

Aristotle had an answer for that, too. He pointed out that all objects were pulled down toward the earth. Anyone who threw an object into the air could see that with his own eyes. Aristotle said this was because the earth was a sphere that attracted all earthly objects to its own center. The direction "down" simply meant "toward the center of the earth."

This meant that wherever you went on earth, "down" was in the direction of your feet. If two people were standing on opposite sides of the earth and could see each other, each would think the other was standing on his head. Each, however, would be sure that he himself was standing straight up.

In fact this, according to Aristotle, was the very reason that the earth was a sphere, not egg-shaped or cigar-shaped. Since everything on earth was pulled down toward the center, all matter on the earth's surface arranged itself to be as near the center as possible. From geometry, it was known that if every portion of the surface of a solid were as close to the center as possible, that solid would have to be a sphere. In fact, one way of defining a sphere is to say that it is a solid with the property that every point on its surface is equally distant from its center.

From the time of Aristotle, most educated men in the western world believed the earth was round. During the Middle Ages there was a decline in scientific thinking, but the knowledge of the roundness of the earth did not die out.

Yet until the time of Columbus it was only the few educated people who believed this. Most people continued to believe in the "common-sense" notion that the earth was flat. Even at the time of Columbus a great many people expected that any ship which ventured too far out into the Atlantic Ocean would go over the end of the world.

We ourselves still have a reminder of such beliefs in common phrases such as, "I'll follow you to the ends of the earth."

MEASURING THE WAISTLINE

Granted that the earth is a sphere, how large is it? What is the length of its waistline, so to speak? What is its *circumference?*

The earth is obviously a very large sphere. The larger the sphere, the gentler its curve, and the sphere of the earth has a very gentle curve indeed. It is the gentleness of the curve that makes the earth look so flat when we are standing on the surface and seeing only a little piece of it.

Another proof of its large size is simply that it is possible to take trips thousands of miles long without going completely around the earth.

A Greek astronomer named Eratosthenes of Cyrene, about 230 B.C., thought of a way of measuring the size of the earth without going around it, however.

If the earth were a sphere, as Eratosthenes knew it was, then the sun's rays should strike different parts of it at different angles. For instance, on June 21, the sun was just overhead at noon in the city of Syene in Egypt, so that it cast no shadow there. In Alexandria, Egypt (where Eratosthenes lived) the sun was not quite overhead at that moment, and cast a small shadow.

Eratosthenes knew the distance between Alexandria and Syene. He could use geometry to calculate how much the earth's surface had to curve in that distance to make the difference in the shadows. From this curve he figured out that the distance around the earth was 250,000 "stadia."

Now the "stadion" is a Greek measure of length, and we

are not sure exactly how long it is in miles. Most historians have decided that the "stadion" Eratosthenes used was equal to a tenth of a mile. If so, his figure for the circumference of the earth comes to 25,000 miles, which is just about right.

However, Eratosthenes' figure was not accepted by everybody. In those early days, it just seemed too large. At that time the known area of the world stretched from Spain to India and from Great Britain to Ethiopia. That was about 7,500 miles east and west and 4,500 miles north and south. (The known area had just about doubled in the four centuries since the Greeks had first begun to wonder if the earth might not be a sphere.)

Even so, if the earth were really 25,000 miles in circumference, that meant that about five-sixths of it was still unknown. Geographers couldn't imagine what to do with all that unknown stretch of the earth. Could it be all ocean? That seemed wasteful. Some made up continents to fill the empty stretches. Others thought the earth simply couldn't be that large, and that was all there was to it.

About 100 B.C., a geographer named Posidonius of Apamea measured the earth over again by Eratosthenes' method and somehow came out with the answer that it was only 18,000 miles in circumference. That seemed a more comfortable size. The 18,000 mile figure was adopted by Claudius Ptolemaeus (usually known simply as Ptolemy), who was the last great geographer and astronomer of the ancient world. He lived about 150 A.D.

During the Middle Ages, the Arabs and then the West Europeans used Ptolemy's books as the great authorities on geography and astronomy, so the small figure for the earth's circumference remained popular.

Then, between 1275 and 1295 A.D., an Italian named Marco Polo traveled throughout China and, when he came back, wrote an immensely popular book about it. Polo's travels showed that land stretched from Spain to China for a distance of about 12,000 miles at least, and that to the east of China there was an ocean.

If the world were a sphere, then the ocean to the east of China could be the same as the ocean to the west of Europe. Perhaps one could cross that ocean. Then, instead of traveling east for 12,000 miles of hard land journey, one might sail west instead over a much smaller distance of ocean.

An Italian geographer named Paolo Toscanelli thought this was indeed possible. He believed in the small figure of the earth's circumference. In 1474 he published a map which showed that the ocean voyage from Spain to China was only between three and four thousand miles long.

THE OCEAN VOYAGES

Toscanelli's maps and theories fired the imagination of an Italian navigator named Cristoforo Colombo. (He is better known to us by the Latin version of his name, Christopher Columbus.) Columbus tried to get various nations to finance an expedition westward into the Atlantic.

At the Court of Portugal, Columbus was turned down. Most of us are told that this was because the Portuguese geographers thought the earth was flat, but this is not so. They knew it was round.

In fact, at that time the Portuguese were the most skillful navigators in Europe, and their ships had just reached the southern tip of Africa. Their geographers were rather of the opinion that the earth was larger than Toscanelli said it was. They believed that in order to reach China and India, Columbus would have to sail at least 12,000 miles westward, not 3,000. They knew that a 12,000 mile journey in the sailing ships of those days was impractical, so they advised the Portuguese king to keep on trying for the around-Africa route and not waste his money on the Atlantic.

In a way, the Portuguese geographers were right. Columbus never did reach India, whereas the Portuguese reached it as a result of Vasco da Gama's successful voyage in 1497.

Columbus, however, got Spain to finance the trip and to supply him with three small ships and a crew of jailbirds. (They were the only ones who could be made to head out into the ocean.) Columbus would indeed have had to travel 12,000 miles to reach Asia and would surely have perished— but the American continents were in the way.

Nobody had dreamed they existed and Columbus, who was completely wrong, won immortal fame by accident. To the day he died, however, he still believed he had reached Asia.

The man who finally accomplished what Columbus had thought he was going to do was Ferdinand Magellan. He was a Portuguese navigator who served under the flag of Spain.

Portugal had reached India by going east around Africa, and Spain had reached only the savage and primitive Americas by going west across the Atlantic. In 1493 Pope Alexander VI, to avoid troubles and wars between Spain and Portugal, got Spain to agree to stay west of a certain line down the middle of the Atlantic, and Portugal to stay east.

It looked as though Portugal had far the better of the bargain, so Spain thought again of Columbus' theory of reaching Asia by traveling to the west. They would be staying on the western side of the Pope's line. The only trouble was that they would have to go farther than Columbus had planned. They would have to get past the Americas somehow and keep on going.

In August, 1519, Magellan set out with five ships to do that job. He crossed the Atlantic and sailed down the coast of South America, looking for some sea passage through the continent. He had to travel almost to the very tip of South America before he found the Straits of Magellan (still called by his name to this day).

On the other side of the straits was the largest ocean of the world. It had been discovered seven years before in Panama and had been named the "South Sea." Magellan renamed it the Pacific Ocean because of the fair weather he experienced, after the storms of the straits. ("Pacific" means "peaceful.")

Magellan and his crew were the first men to sail completely across the empty thousands of miles of the Pacific. They suffered terribly from lack of food and water. Many of them died of scurvy. But Magellan held on with an iron will, fighting down mutiny and driving his ships and men onward. They finally reached Guam, where they were able to get fresh provisions. They then discovered the Philippines. (The name was given to it some years later, in honor of Philip II of Spain.)

Thus Magellan finally reached Asian waters by sailing westward; but in the Philippines he was killed.

By this time only two of Magellan's ships were left, and they continued westward across the Indian Ocean. They reached Africa and sailed around it from east to west, then up the west coast and back to Spain. Only one ship and eighteen half-dead survivors, under the leadership of Juan Sebastian del Cano, returned to Spain in July, 1522, after a voyage of three years. That voyage was as difficult for those days as a trip to the moon would be in our own time.

Those eighteen were the first men ever to circumnavigate the earth, to go completely around the sphere. They proved once and for all that the earth *was* a sphere, and a large one. They showed that Ptolemy and Toscanelli (and Columbus too) had all been wrong about the earth's circumference, and that it was well over 18,000 miles.

It wasn't until 1671, however, that the size of the earth was finally established with fair accuracy. A French astronomer named Jean Picard made careful measurements with the use of the telescope, an instrument the ancient Greeks didn't have. As a result, scientists returned to Eratosthenes' original measurement, and there they have stayed ever since.

The circumference of the earth at the equator is now known to be 24,897 miles. The distance straight through the earth (its *diameter*) can be calculated from the circumference. The diameter from one point on the equator to a point on the equator directly opposite is 7,928 miles. (To get that figure, if you are curious, you must divide the circumference by the quantity "pi," which is approximately equal to 3.14159.)

TWO

NOT QUITE A SPHERE

IT MOVES, ANYWAY

Another matter about the earth which seems to go against common sense is that it is not just a sphere, but a spinning sphere. It is *rotating,* making a complete turn every twenty-four hours.

To the early star-gazers in Egypt and Babylonia, it seemed that the earth stood still and that the sky, with its stars and other heavenly bodies, moved about the earth from east to west once every twenty-four hours. Certainly, this seems to make sense. Certainly, no one would dare say our solid earth was moving.

Of course, you know, it is hard to tell, sometimes, whether we are standing still or not. Suppose you are in a train at a station with another train on the neighboring track. Suddenly the train next to you starts to inch slowly backward. You are sure your train is standing still and the other train is moving. But then you look out the other window and you find that the station, trees, ground and all, are also moving backward. Well, this can't be so, so you decide that the other train, along with everything else, is standing still and it is your own train that is moving forward, after all.

But suppose your train and the neighboring one were all you could see. How would you decide then which train was moving? It would be difficult.

That is the position the early stargazers were in. They could see only the sky and the earth and it just seemed to make sense to suppose the earth was standing still when they, standing on the earth, felt no movement.

However, as the Greek astronomers began to get some idea of the size of the universe, they became doubtful. For reasons I will explain later in the book, they began to suspect that the moon was hundreds of thousands of miles away. They also suspected that the moon was the closest of the heavenly bodies, so that the other ones must be incredibly far away. This meant the stars would have to sweep through a mighty circle at a speed of many millions of miles an hour, perhaps, to get around the earth in twenty-four hours.

It seemed much more reasonable to suppose that the earth was itself turning, even though we couldn't feel the motion, while the heavens stood still.

The first astronomer who is known to have believed this was the Greek, Heraclides Ponticus, in 350 B.C.

This notion, however, did not really take hold at the time. One could prove by measurements that the earth was a sphere, but there was no measurement that could show the earth was spinning; there were only theoretical arguments. (Incidentally, the first man to show by means of actual measurements that the earth was spinning was a French physicist named Jean B. L. Foucault. And he didn't do it till 1851, more than two thousand years after Heraclides Ponticus had advanced the theory.)

During the Middle Ages, especially, the notion of the spinning earth seemed wrong. For one thing, the Bible stated that, during a certain battle, the Israelite commander Joshua had ordered the sun and moon to stand still so the battle might be completed and won. Didn't this imply that it was the heavens which moved, not the earth?

Besides, if the earth were spinning (some people argued) there would be a terrific wind. And if you jumped upward, you would come down in a different place. Birds flying from their nests would be swept away and never find their way back—and so on.

In 1543, however, the Polish astronomer, Nicholas Copernicus, published a book which worked out the mathematical details of a system in which the earth and the other planets moved about the sun. Gradually this view won out and the earth was accepted as just one small planet among many others. So it began to seem quite ridiculous to imagine a whole immense universe circling about one small planet every twenty-four hours. Anyone who accepted the Copernican system had to believe the earth was spinning.

And there is no wind because the air moves with the earth. Besides, to give you a familiar example, if you were standing on a speeding train and jumped up, you would come down on the same spot, since you were moving with the train. You would not even be aware of the train's motion, except for its swaying and vibration. Since the earth moves without swaying or vibrating, you are not aware of the earth's rotation at all.

Yet even as late as 1633 the Italian scientist Galileo Galilei usually known by his first name only) was forced by Church authorities to admit he was wrong in thinking that the earth moved. Afterward he is supposed to have muttered under his breath, "But it moves, anyway."

The earth does indeed move anyway, and no educated person has doubted it since Galileo's time.

And yet as soon as it was definitely established that the earth was rotating, people began wondering if Earth were really a sphere after all. That is, if it were really *exactly* a sphere. Exactly.

THE BULGING GLOBE

To begin with, can we say the earth is exactly a sphere

when it is broken up into mountains and valleys? The lowest point on the earth's land surface is at the shores of the Dead Sea in Israel, where the earth's surface is 1,286 feet (a quarter of a mile) below sea level. The highest mountain peak is Mt. Everest in the Himalayas, which is 29,002 feet (5½ miles) above sea level.

How serious are these departures from perfection? Suppose we made an exact model of the earth six feet in diameter (as tall as a tall man) with all its mountains and valleys, all its continents and oceans in exact proportion. The oceans would, of course, be smooth. The continents, however, would be rough and uneven. Or should be. But actually, on the six-foot globe, Mt. Everest would only be 1/20 of an inch higher than sea level, and the Dead Sea would be less than 1/400 of an inch below sea level.

Thus you would never be aware of the unevennesses. Even so, when astronomers talk of the shape of the earth, they like to pretend it is covered with one big ocean. Such an all-sea-level world would have no unevennesses at all. Would it then be a perfect sphere?

In 1671 the English scientist, Isaac Newton, suggested an answer to that question. The answer was no. Newton was working out his theory of universal gravitation then, and had not yet published it. Nor was he going to for another twelve years, because he had certain mathematical difficulties to overcome first. However, as far as gravitation applied to the earth, Newton went along with old Aristotle.

The earth pulled everything toward its center with strong force and so it formed itself into a sphere. Or at least it would if the gravity that pulled toward the center were the only force that was involved. Newton, however, knew of another force which could pull in the direction opposite from gravity.

Thus if you held a pail of water upside down over your head, gravity would pull the water out of the pail and all over your head. If however, you swung the pail smoothly in a circle, over your head and down again, not a drop of water would fall out even when the pail was upside down. (Don't try this unless you're in the back yard and wearing a raincoat. It takes practice.)

The force that holds the water in the pail is called *centrifugal force.*

You can see how centrifugal force works if you own a small ball to which an elastic string is attached. Hold the free end of the elastic and swing the ball, not too quickly. Centrifugal force will force the ball away from the center of the circle, which is your hand, and the elastic will stretch and be taut. (In fact, "centrifugal" comes from Latin words meaning "fleeing from the center.")

If you swing more rapidly, the centrifugal force becomes stronger and the elastic stretches. If you swing rapidly enough, the centrifugal force will break the elastic and away the ball will fly. This shows that the faster an object spins, the stronger the centrifugal force acting on it.

The earth is spinning, too, but, as a result of the spin, different points on its surface move at different speeds.

You see, the earth spins about a certain imaginary line called the *axis of rotation.* One end of this axis is the *north pole,* the other end the *south pole.* A line going around the earth exactly halfway between the poles is called the *equator.*

(If you wish, you can make a model of the spinning earth by sticking a knitting needle through an apple and twisting the ends of the knitting needle. The next few paragraphs may be clearer then.)

All spots on the surface of the earth move about the axis in a complete circle in twenty-four hours. However, a spot near the poles makes only a small circle, while a spot farther from the poles makes a larger circle. Since in both cases the circle is completed in twenty-four hours, a point on the

surface far from the poles must move more quickly than a
point on the surface near the poles.

As a matter of fact, the pinpoints on the map that are the
north pole and the south pole do not move at all as the earth
spins. They are like the center of a wheel's hubcap. On the
other hand, a spot on the equator, such as the city of Quito,
in Ecuador, must move fastest of all, since it is as far from
both poles as it is possible to get. Quito must cover 24,897
miles in twenty-four hours, so it travels 1,037 miles an hour.

The city of Los Angeles, which is a third of the way from
the equator to the north pole, moves more slowly than
Quito, 850 miles an hour. New York, halfway to the north
pole, moves more slowly still, 700 miles an hour. Murmansk, a

Rotation at Different Speeds

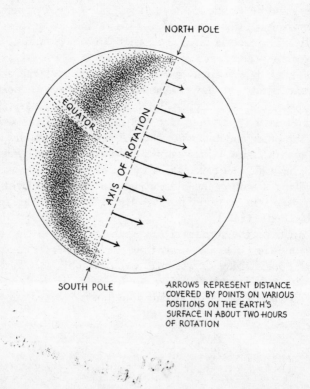

ARROWS REPRESENT DISTANCE
COVERED BY POINTS ON VARIOUS
POSITIONS ON THE EARTH'S
SURFACE IN ABOUT TWO HOURS
OF ROTATION

city in the Soviet Union which is two-thirds of the way to the north pole, moves at only 400 miles an hour.

As the earth spins, it develops centrifugal force which tends to move its surface out away from the center, against the pull of gravity. Near the poles the centrifugal force is very small, so that Murmansk hardly lifts at all against gravity. New York lifts up farther, Los Angeles still farther and Quito farthest of all.

In short, Newton suggested that the earth bulged outward because of the centrifugal force of its spin. He said it bulged out more and more as the equator is approached, and bulged out most of all right at the equator.

It is as though you were to imagine the earth made out of rubber and just lightly pressed between a giant finger and

An Oblate Spheroid

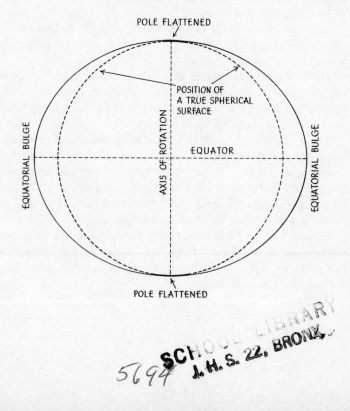

thumb at the north and south poles. The poles would flatten out a tiny bit and the equatorial regions would bulge out a tiny bit.

Such an out-of-shape sphere is called an *oblate spheroid*. ("Oblate" comes from Latin words meaning "sides sticking out.") An oblate spheroid is flattened at the poles and has an *equatorial bulge*.

THE PENDULUM PROVES IT

Newton didn't have to work completely in the dark on this, or rely only on his theories. There was one very good argument for the oblate spheroid theory in the heavens. By 1671, telescopes were good enough to magnify Jupiter and Saturn into sizable globes. Both planets spin much more quickly than the earth does. They should therefore show considerable flattening at the poles and considerable bulging in the equatorial regions.

And they do, indeed. The flattening and the bulges can be clearly seen just by looking. The two planets, especially Saturn, look distinctly oval.

There was another piece of evidence that quickly showed up, too. Not in the heavens, either, but on the earth itself. It involved the *pendulum*, which is a weight that swings freely at the end of a string, wire or rod.

It was Galileo who, about 1581, discovered that a particular pendulum always took the same time to make a complete swing, whether that swing was a wide one or a narrow one. Furthermore the time for a swing depended on the length of the pendulum. A long pendulum took a longer time to make a swing than a short pendulum did.

It turned out, for instance, that a pendulum just a little over thirty-nine inches long (from the center of the weight to the point of attachment) would complete its swing, wide or narrow, in just one second.

Such a pendulum could be used to run a clock. By 1656 the Dutch astronomer Christiaan Huyghens had built the first pendulum clock. Accurate timekeeping dates only from then.

Now it is the force of gravity that keeps a pendulum swinging. If you pull the weight of a pendulum to one side it must move upward, too. When you let go, gravity pulls the weight down and the force of its movement carries it over to the other side and up again. Gravity pulls it down once more, and this repeats over and over.

If gravity were stronger than it was, the weight of a pendulum would be pulled down harder, and its swing would be completed in less time. If gravity were weaker, the swing would take more time.

Newton maintained that gravitational force depended partly upon the distance between the centers of the two bodies involved. The greater the distance, the weaker the force. The rate at which a particular pendulum swung depended, therefore, on its distance from the center of the earth.

If the earth were a perfect sphere, the gravitational force would be the same everywhere on the earth's surface, because all points on the surface of a perfect sphere are equally distant from the center. A particular pendulum would in that case swing at the same rate everywhere.

But if you carry a pendulum up into the mountains, it is then a bit farther from the earth's center and swings under the influence of weaker gravity. The pendulum therefore swings a trifle more slowly on mountain heights.

In 1673 a French scientific expedition in French Guiana found that the pendulum of their clock, which beat out perfect seconds in Paris, was moving slightly slower in their tropical headquarters—as compared with the steady motion of the stars. It was as though they had carried their pendulum to mountain heights, and yet their camp was at sea level.

When Isaac Newton heard of this, he said at once this

showed that French Guiana was mountain-high. That country
was 3,000 miles nearer the equator than Paris was—almost
on the equator, in fact—and was therefore almost at the
highest part of the equatorial bulge. Naturally, the pendulum
would be farther from the earth's center and would beat
more slowly. The equatorial bulge was thus proved a reality.

But now that I have mentioned the pendulum, I want to
change the subject for just a moment to describe another type
of proof that resulted from its use. At the beginning of the
chapter I said Foucault had proved that the earth was
rotating. He did this in 1851 by using a pendulum.

The laws of mechanics make it plain that if a pendulum
is left completely to itself, it will swing back and forth in the
same straight line forever.

Foucault pointed out that this would happen if the earth
were motionless. However, if the earth were rotating, the
pendulum ought to seem to twist its direction of motion.
(Actually, the pendulum wouldn't really twist. It would be
the surface of the earth that was itself twisting as the earth
rotated. The pendulum would be staying in the same straight
line. It would then seem to twist, just as the stars seem to
move. In both cases, the earth's motion would really be
responsible.)

The way in which the pendulum's line of motion would
seem to twist would depend on its position on the earth. At the
equator, there would be no twist at all. North of the equator
the twist would be in one direction; south of the equator
in the opposite direction. The rate of twist would grow
faster and faster as one moved farther from the equator. At
the poles themselves the line of motion would twist in a
complete circle in twenty-four hours. At Paris, the complete
turn would take place only after thirty-two hours.

Foucault prepared to test this. He suspended a large iron
ball about two feet in diameter from a steel wire more than

two hundred feet long, under the dome of a church in Paris. Every attempt was made to keep the air and the building free of vibrations that might disturb the steady swing of this tremendous pendulum.

The iron ball was drawn far to one side and tied to the wall by a cord. Then the cord was set on fire. As it broke, down swung the ball, without the vibration that would have been caused if a hand had let it go.

The floor of the church had been sprinkled with sand and, as the ball swung down, a spike attached to its bottom swung just close enough to make a mark in the sand. That mark showed the line along which the pendulum was swinging.

As time went on, and the pendulum swung back and forth, the direction of the mark slowly changed. It twisted in just the way and at just the speed it was expected to. The simplest explanation of this was that the earth was rotating under the pendulum. This view of things has been accepted by everyone.

The experiment caused great excitement at the time, and Foucault won great fame as the first man who actually proved that the earth was rotating. Of course, no one had doubted the fact for two hundred years before Foucault, but it was nice to have the proof of it, anyway.

MEASUREMENT OF THE DEGREE

But let's get back to Newton and to the shape of the earth. The case of the pendulum in French Guiana was enough for Newton, but others still doubted. More definite proof seemed needed, and that came about through a direct measurement of how the earth curved. The way this is done needs some explanation.

The circumference of a circle is measured in *degrees of arc*. Imagine yourself standing at the center of a circle with one arm pointing toward a mark on the circumference. Now swing your arm toward another point. In doing so, your arm has moved through an angle and that angle measures the length of the portion of the circumference (called an *arc*) that you have covered with the sweep of your arm.

Suppose you had turned completely around and pointed toward the original mark again. You turn through an angle of 360 degrees in one complete revolution, so the complete circumference of a circle is 360 degrees of arc long.

Half the circumference of a circle is 180 degrees of arc. A quarter of the circumference is 90 degrees of arc, and so on.

The actual length of a degree of arc depends on the size of the circle. A degree of arc is always 1/360 of the complete circumference of the circle. A small circle with a circumference of 36 inches has a degree of arc that is only one-tenth of an inch long. In a larger circle, with a circumference of

Divisions of the Circle

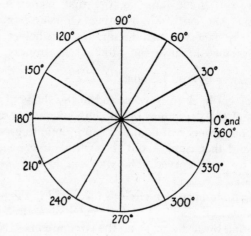

sixty feet, a degree of arc is two inches long. In a circle as large as the earth's equator, a degree of arc is just about sixty-nine miles long.

It is possible to calculate the circumference of a particular circle by measuring the amount of curvature present in a small part of it. The less the curvature, the larger the circumference.

This is a good thing, since the circumference of the earth is so great that we could never measure it by putting a tape measure around it. We must, instead, measure the curvature of a small part of it.

This is done by measuring accurate straight lines, several miles long, along its surface, and arranging them in triangles. If the earth were absolutely flat, the three angles of such triangles would add up to just 180 degrees. If the earth were curved, they would add up to more than 180 degrees. The greater the curvature, the higher the sum of the angles.

By summing the angles, then, the curvature can be determined and the circumference of the earth can be calculated. Since 1/360 of the circumference is a degree of arc, this system can be considered as measuring a degree of arc on the earth's surface. It was this system, by the way, that Jean Picard used (as mentioned at the end of chapter 1) to make the first accurate measurement of the earth's circumference.

In a perfect circle, the length of a degree of arc is the same at all points along the circumference. The equator is just about a perfect circle, so a degree of arc measured along any part of it is the same as one along any other part of it.

Suppose, though, you had a flattened circle; a type of closed curve called an *ellipse*. The flattened part on top and bottom has less curvature than the bulging parts on the sides. If you were to measure the curvature of the flattened part you would end up with a long degree of arc. The curvature along the bulging parts would give you a short degree of arc.

If the earth were flattened at the poles and bulging at the equator, then a line circling the earth from north pole to south pole and back would be an ellipse. (Such a line is called a *meridian of longitude*.) A degree measured along the length of such a meridian would get slowly larger as one approached the pole, if the earth were really an oblate spheroid.

In the early 1700's, degrees were measured along a meridian in France. But the north-south distance wasn't great enough to make much difference, and the results were doubtful.

So in 1735 two French expeditions set out. One went to Peru, near the equator. The other went to Lapland near the north pole. Both expeditions took years and made many careful measurements. It turned out that, in Peru, a degree of latitude was equal to about 68.7 miles, while in Lapland it was equal to 69.5 miles.

Newton had turned out to be correct, and the earth was indeed an oblate spheroid.

Many measurements have been taken since then, and by 1957 the measurements of the earth were believed to be as follows:

The *polar diameter* (that is, the distance through the earth from the north pole to the south pole) is 7,902 miles.

The *equatorial diameter* (the distance through the earth from a point on the equator to another point on the equator directly opposite) is 7,928 miles.

The difference is twenty-six miles, or just about 1/300 of the total diameter. The equatorial bulge is thus thirteen miles high all around the earth. This is not much, really. If our six-foot model of the earth were built to show this flattening, and the equatorial diameter were exactly six feet, the polar diameter would be five feet, eleven and 3/4 inches.

The flattening is so little that from space the earth (unlike Jupiter and Saturn) would seem perfectly round to the eye.

And yet the difference is important. If detailed maps of large areas of the earth were drawn up on the assumption that the earth is a perfect sphere, the maps would be wrong by several miles in various spots. This could make a big difference to ships or planes (or, alas, missiles) trying to find a particular city or island.

Even as it is, there was difficulty in getting some positions on earth closer than a mile or two, until unexpected help arrived by way of space science.

The artificial satellite, Vanguard I, was sent up on March 17, 1958. Its solar battery, powered by the sun, has been sending down signals ever since, so that its orbit has been followed for a long time and in exact detail.

If the earth were perfectly spherical, Vanguard I would be pulled by the earth's gravity in the same way wherever in space it was located. But Earth has an equatorial bulge, so its pull is slightly lopsided. Sometimes Vanguard I is over the northern hemisphere; then the extra mass in the equatorial bulge gives the little satellite a yank southward. When Vanguard I is over the southern hemisphere, it gets a northward yank.

These pulls have a complicated effect on the orbit, but astronomers can work from the orbit back to the equatorial bulge. From the orbit they can tell the shape of the bulge better than ever before.

For instance, the equatorial bulge is now known to be 13 1/6 miles high at the equator, a figure which is more exact than ever before. What's more, the bulge is a little more massive south of the equator than north. The southern part of the bulge is up to fifty feet higher than the northern part. At the same time, the north pole is one hundred feet farther from the center of the earth than the south pole is. (All this, of course, refers to sea level.)

As a result of these new determinations of the shape of the earth, new accuracy is possible in maps. The location of American military bases on some islands in the Pacific, for instance, was not known exactly before the satellites were sent up. The measurements were sometimes off by a mile or so. Now their location has been pinpointed to within fifty feet.

And so you see, one of the first results of the new science of space is indeed to get to know our own world better.

THREE

THE LAYERS BENEATH

THE TONS OF EARTH

Once we know the diameter of the earth, it is easy to tell a few other things about it. For instance, its surface area can be calculated by a simple formula. It comes to just about 196,950,000 square miles. This is fifty-five times the area of the United States. The volume of the earth can also be calculated. It is equal to 260,000,000,000 cubic miles.

But one thing we can't determine just from the size of the earth is the amount of matter contained in it. The matter contained in any body is known as its *mass*, so what I am now asking is: what is the mass of the earth?

Knowing the earth's volume is no help, because different amounts of matter can be packed into the same volume. For instance, you can fill a barrel with ping-pong balls and the barrel will contain so little matter you will have no trouble lifting it. But fill another barrel exactly like the first with lead shot, and you couldn't possibly budge it. The contents take up equal volumes in each case, yet the mass of the lead shot is far higher than the mass of the ping-pong balls.

Still, there is a way to find the mass of the earth. To do so, we must use Newton's Law of Universal Gravitation.

Let's consider two bodies—the earth and a lead ball—just as an example. According to Newton's theory, the force of gravitation between two such bodies depends on several things:

(A) the mass of one body (the lead ball)

(B) the mass of the other body (the earth)

(C) the distance between the centers of the two bodies

(D) the value of a quantity called the *gravitational constant.*

If you multiply (A), (B) and (D), divide the product by (C), and then divide the quotient again by (C), you get:

(E) the strength of the gravitational attraction between the two bodies.

That may sound complicated to you, but it really isn't. Besides, we're not going to try to do it. I just want to point out that if in one way or another we know the value of any four of those five items, we can calculate the value of the fifth item by very simple mathematics.

In the case of the lead ball and the earth, which of the items do we know and which don't we know?

First of all, we know the strength of the gravitational attraction between the earth and the lead ball. We get that just by weighing the ball. The mass of the lead ball is also obtained by weighing it. (Scientists have agreed to let the mass of any object equal its weight as measured at sea level at forty-five degrees latitude.)

We also know a third item: the distance between the centers of the lead ball and the earth. That is equal to half the diameter of the earth. So we know items (A), (C) and (E).

But there are two items we don't know. (B) the mass of the earth, and (D) the gravitational constant. Since we only know three of the five items, and not four, mathematics can't help us. We're stuck.

But wait! Newton couldn't tell the value of the gravitational constant. He never did know it to the day he died. However, his theory stated that whatever the value of the gravitational constant, it was the same for any two bodies, any two bodies at all. Why not, then, make use of two bodies of ordinary size and measure the masses, the distance, the attraction between them, everything but the gravitational constant—and then calculate its value from the rest?

This is easy in theory but difficult in practice, because gravity is an extremely weak force. It seems strong to us on the earth, because we are used to the earth's gravity, and the earth is an extremely massive body. But as far as ordinary-sized objects are concerned, gravitational attraction between them is almost nil.

Nevertheless, an English scientist named Henry Cavendish had a go at it in 1798.

This is what he did. He suspended a light rod by a wire to its center. At each end of the rod was a light lead ball. The rod could twist freely about the wire, but he let it come to rest and measured the position.

Next, very carefully, he brought two large lead balls near opposite sides of the two small ones. The large balls attracted

Measuring the Mass of the Earth

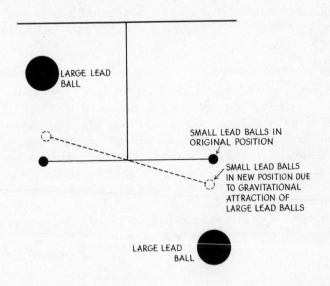

LARGE LEAD BALL

SMALL LEAD BALLS IN ORIGINAL POSITION

SMALL LEAD BALLS IN NEW POSITION DUE TO GRAVITATIONAL ATTRACTION OF LARGE LEAD BALLS

LARGE LEAD BALL

the small balls with a tiny gravitational pull. In consequence, each small ball moved very slightly toward the large ball and the rod twisted about the wire slightly.

From the amount of the twist Cavendish was able to calculate the amount of the gravitational pull. Since Cavendish also knew the masses of the small balls and the large ones and the distances between their centers, he now had items (A), (B), (C) and (E). The only item he didn't have was (D), the gravitational constant. Knowing four items, he could easily calculate the fifth, and he did that at once. Cavendish was the first man ever to calculate the gravitational constant.

If we go back to the problem of the lead ball and the earth, we can now add the value of the gravitational constant to the list of items we know. The only thing left unknown is the mass of the earth. Since the other four items are known, the mass of the earth can be calculated at once.

This Cavendish also did, and he found the mass of the earth to be 6,600,000,000,000,000,000,000 tons. This is a tremendous figure, but it was worked out by observing the slight movement of a small lead ball toward a large one. In making this tiny measurement, Cavendish had "weighed the earth."

STONES FROM THE SKY

Once Cavendish had worked out the mass of the earth, he was able to calculate the average density of it.

Density is a figure which tells you how much mass is contained in a certain definite volume of some particular substance. For instance, since a cubic foot of water has a mass of 62.43 pounds, the density of water is 62.43 pounds per cubic foot. The density of mercury, as another example, is 850 pounds per cubic foot.

Another way of stating density is to give the number of ounces of mass contained in a cubic inch of the substance.

The density of water is 0.578 ounces per cubic inch, which means that a cubic inch of water has a mass of 0.578 ounces. The density of mercury is 7.9 ounces per cubic inch.

Scientists, however, don't usually measure in pounds, ounces, cubic feet and cubic inches. Instead, they make use of a system of measurements called the *metric system,* invented in France in 1791.

In the metric system, volume is measured in *cubic centimeters*. This is a small volume, equal to less than 1/16 of a cubic inch. Mass is measured in *grams,* which is also a small unit, being less than 1/28 of an ounce.

However, the metric system is very logically arranged, and one of its convenient arrangements is that 1 cubic centimeter of water has a mass of just about 1 gram. The density of water is therefore 1.00 grams per cubic centimeter; or, to abbreviate it, 1.00 gm/cc. Using this system, the density of mercury is 13.5 gm/cc.

Once we know the mass of the earth in tons (thanks to Cavendish), that mass can easily be changed over into grams. Every ton contains 907,185 grams. In the same way the earth's volume can easily be calculated as so many cubic centimeters instead of as so many cubic miles.

If this is done, it turns out that there are 5.52 grams of mass in the earth for every cubic centimeter it contains. The average density of the earth is thus 5.52 gm/cc.

But this is only the average density. The earth is made up of all kinds of rocks. Some are quite dense and some are much less dense. Still, we can take an average of the density of the earth's outermost rocks, those which we can reach and handle, measure and weigh. We can compare their average density with the figure Cavendish obtained for the earth as a whole. When this is done, it turns out that the outermost rocks of the earth's globe have an average density of only 2.8 gm/cc.

This can only mean that the interior regions of the earth, which we can't reach and handle, must be quite dense to bring the density of the whole earth up to average.

It is impossible to reach down and inspect the deep interior of the earth. However, it is possible to make some reasonable deductions.

One of the pieces of evidence that made deductions possible came from the skies.

Just about the time Cavendish was determining the mass of the earth, scientists were beginning to wonder if it could be true that objects might fall from the sky.

Almost everyone has seen "shooting stars." These are lines of light that form in the sky occasionally. The lights are called *meteors*, from a Greek work meaning "something high in the air."

Sometimes there were reports that after a flash in the sky, a rock or a piece of metal that had not been there before was found in a field. Every once in a while some farmer would bring such a specimen to some learned man and tell this story. At first scientists simply refused to believe these stories.

It wasn't till after 1800 that some astronomers began to say that falling stones might be more than just a tall story. Meteors could be flashes made when a piece of matter struck the atmosphere and then heated to a white-hot glow, as a result of friction with the air. Small meteors would evaporate in the process. Larger ones might survive in part. The fragment that hit the ground might then be called a *meteorite*. (The "-ite" ending is usually used for minerals found in the ground.)

President Thomas Jefferson made a famous remark about this theory. He heard reports that two professors in Connecticut had found such a meteorite and claimed to have witnessed its fall. Jefferson said, "I could more easily believe that two

Yankee professors would lie than that stones would fall from Heaven."

But in 1833 the earth underwent bombardment from a tremendous number of such stones. During the night of November 12, the whole sky above the eastern United States turned into a rocket display of countless meteors. Astronomers turned enthusiastically to meteor studies, and it soon turned out that Thomas Jefferson (who had died seven years too soon to see the great meteor display) was wrong in this case.

Two types of meteorites were discovered. One type is the *stony meteorite*, made up mostly of stone, as you would guess from the name. The other is the *iron meteorite*. This is metal, made up, on the average, of about 91 per cent iron, 8.5 per cent nickel and 0.5 per cent cobalt. (Nickel and cobalt are metals that closely resemble iron.)

Now where do meteorites come from? Originally they must have been moving about in space. Occasionally one collides with the earth. Can they be the remnants of some other planet far out in space that exploded many millions of years ago? Some astronomers began to think this might be what happened, especially since there were thousands of tiny planets between the orbits of Mars and Jupiter. That is where the planet might have exploded.

If so, the stony meteorites may be pieces of the outer parts of the planet; and the iron meteorites may be pieces of the inner portion.

This makes sense. The density of iron is 7.86 gm/cc, which is higher than the average density of the earth. Perhaps the earth is chiefly stone outside, with a low density; and chiefly iron inside, with a high density. Then the average density of the earth could well come to some in-between value.

But how much of the earth is stone and how much iron? For an answer to that, scientists turned to the study of earthquakes.

The Trembling Earth

The outermost portion of the earth is cracked in places. These cracks are called *faults*. There is always a certain amount of strain at these faults. Occasionally the earth readjusts itself slightly, and there is a sliding of rock against rock at these faults.

When this happens, the earth trembles or quakes, and we call the result an *earthquake* for that reason. Earthquakes set up vibrations of various types that travel through the earth (and are sometimes strong enough to destroy cities). Some types of earthquake vibrations travel along the surface of the earth. Others travel straight through the body of the earth, reaching great depths, and coming out again at a point on the surface that may be thousands of miles from the central point (or *epicenter*) of the earthquake.

Each type of vibration travels at its own speed. When a vibration comes to a point where the structure of the earth suddenly changes (from solid to liquid, perhaps, or from stone to metal, or even just from one kind of stone to another kind), the vibration changes direction and speed suddenly. It will even set up new vibrations at that point, which will then travel off in a new direction altogether.

At various places on the earth, scientists have set up instruments called *seismographs* (from Greek words meaning "earthquake writing"). These instruments are anchored in the solid rock of the earth, and when that rock trembles even very slightly, so does the instrument. A needle which holds steady, while the instrument quivers, makes a wavering mark on a roll of paper attached to the seismograph. (Nowadays a record is made by means of an electric current, instead.) The earthquake writes its own record, as the name implies.

Seismographs in various places will each record the different vibrations that reach them from one particular earthquake. When each station reports the time at which each particular type of vibration arrived, it is usually possible to calculate the routes through the earth taken by each one. If there are sharp bends in the routes, these can be found. In this way boundary lines between layers of different materials deep in the earth can be detected, and their position located.

Scientists still do not agree on all the details of what the earth's interior is like. However, there are some general conclusions with which most agree.

The center of the earth is indeed occupied by a mass of iron (plus some nickel and cobalt), as was guessed from meteorite studies. This is the *iron core* and it is about 3,600 miles in diameter. The temperature is known to get steadily

Internal Structure of the Earth

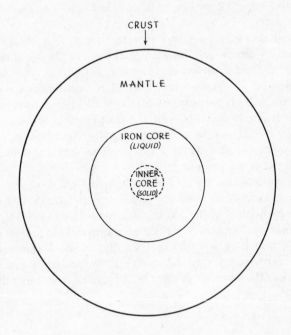

higher as depth beneath the earth's surface increases. At the depth of the iron core, the temperature is high enough to keep that core liquid. (Some scientists, however, suspect that a thousand-mile thickness or so at the very center of the core may be solid.)

The density of the core is higher than the 7.86 gm/cc of ordinary iron. The core, after all, is under the pressure of thousands of miles of rock above it. This squeezes the iron together so that more mass occupies a given volume. Where the iron core starts the density may already be 9 gm/cc and at the very center of the earth it may reach as high as 17 gm/cc. The average density of the core is probably about 11 gm/cc.

The iron core makes up about sixteen per cent of the volume of the whole earth. However, because it is denser than the rest of the earth, so that a larger quantity of mass is squeezed into it, it makes up about thirty-one per cent of the earth's mass.

Above the iron core and surrounding it is a stony layer making up almost all the rest of the earth. It is called the *mantle* (a word meaning an outer garment). The mantle is composed of denser rocks than those with which we are acquainted. Near the surface of the earth, the density of the mantle is about 3 gm/cc, but the deeper parts are squeezed together by the weight of the upper parts. Near the bottom of the mantle, the density is 6 gm/cc. The average density of the mantle is 4.5 gm/cc.

The earth seems to be built much like an egg, therefore. The iron core is its central "yolk," and the stony mantle is the surrounding "white." The earth even has something that resembles an "eggshell," for about the mantle is a thin layer of rock which is less dense than the rock of the mantle. This outermost layer is the earth's *crust*, and it is the crust which has the average density of 2.8 gm/cc that I mentioned earlier.

Back in 1909 a Serbian scientist, A. Mohorovicic, reported that when earthquake waves penetrated a certain depth below the surface, they reached a region where they suddenly began to travel more quickly. There seemed to be a sharp dividing line involved. Above the line, where the earthquake vibrations traveled slowly, was the crust; below, where they traveled quickly, was the mantle.

The line between the two is called the *Mohorovicic discontinuity*. The difficult Serbian name is sometimes abbreviated to "Moho."

Later investigations showed the crust to be thinner under the oceans than under the continents. The Moho discontinuity is about twenty miles deep under the continents and is up to forty miles deep under the great mountain ranges.

The Thickness of the Crust

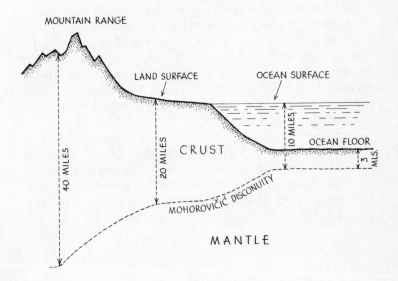

Under the oceans, however, the Moho discontinuity may be only ten miles below the surface. Since the ocean itself is up to six miles deep, there are places where only three or four miles of solid crust exist above the mantle.

Scientists are now making plans to find places in the ocean where the solid crust is only a few miles thick and to drill completely through it to the mantle. This would be a difficult job because first the drill would have to be sunk to the very bottom of the deepest part of the ocean. Then, starting from there, it would have to drill farther than any drill has ever drilled before.

If it succeeded, though, and the Moho discontinuity were reached, scientists would actually see samples of the mantle for the first time ever. A great deal might be learned about the earth's structure that we do not yet know, and may never learn otherwise. (The hole to the Moho discontinuity is being talked about, a little slangily, as the "Mohole.")

Let's imagine our perfect six-foot model of the earth again. At its center would be the iron core, 2.6 feet across. Around it would be the mantle, about 1.7 feet thick all around the core. At the surface would be the crust. The crust would be thin indeed, for it would only be 0.1 inch thick on the average. It might be up to 0.4 inch thick under the Andes and Himalayas and it would dwindle to 0.03 inches under parts of the ocean.

In proportion to the earth, the crust is far thinner than an eggshell is for an egg. An eggshell contains about ten per cent of the mass of the egg. The crust contains only 0.4 per cent of the earth's mass. Just the same all life has been built upon the crust and depends upon it, and it is the only part of the solid earth anyone has ever seen.

FOUR

OUTSIDE THE CRUST

THE HOLLOW SPHERE

The solid part of the earth, including the core, the mantle and the crust, taken all together, is called the *lithosphere*. This comes from the Greek and means "ball of stone." It isn't quite an accurate name because the iron core is not stone. However, all the parts we can see are stone.

The lithosphere makes up 3999/4000 of the mass of the earth. The remaining 1/4000 is very important, however, for it is mostly water, and life could not exist without water.

Although the water on earth forms so small a portion of the planet it is all confined to the surface. To us, who can only see the surface, it looks as though almost all the world is water. Out of a total area of almost 197,000,000 square miles, fully 140,000,000 square miles (or seventy per cent) is covered by water. There is only 57,000,000 square miles of dry land. The Pacific Ocean alone covers almost an entire hemisphere of the earth, with only a few islands to break the monotony of water.

In fact, suppose we imagined the lithosphere were to vanish, leaving only the earth's water behind, untouched. The ocean would enclose almost the entire spot where the lithosphere used to be, forming a hollow sphere. There would be holes in this ball where the continents used to be; smaller holes where islands were.

About ninety-eight per cent of all the water on the earth

would be in this huge spherical ocean. There is an estimated 328,000,000 cubic miles of salt water making it up. Two of the "holes" in the ocean (where Greenland and Antarctica are located) would be covered over with a thick layer of ice, in some places several miles thick. There would be other small patches of ice in mountain glaciers, and a thin layer over the Arctic Ocean. All the ice on the earth comes to about 5,500,000 cubic miles.

A close look at the "holes" in the ocean would show patches of fresh water, making up lakes and rivers in the continent as well as a thin layer of seeping groundwater. The total amount of fresh water present on land comes to 120,000 cubic miles.

There would be almost nowhere on the earth's surface where there wouldn't be some water. Really, then, the water would form a complete ball, just about, and for this reason the earth's water is often spoken of as the *hydrosphere*. This word comes from the Greek and means "ball of water."

Although all this water seems enormous to us, we must always remember that it is only a small amount compared to the globe of the earth. The ocean averages two miles deep, and is up to seven miles deep in spots, but how does this look on our six-foot model of the earth?

On such a model, the oceans would represent a thin film of moisture 1/50 inch thick on the average; and only 1/16 inch thick at the most. If you were leaning against the six-foot model, you probably would not even notice that it was a tiny bit damp.

Yet life originated in the ocean, and eighty-five per cent of all living matter is still to be found in the ocean today. That portion of life which inhabits the "dry land" depends constantly on the fact that "dry land" is not really dry, but contains water. We should be very thankful to the thin film of dampness clinging to the earth.

THE SPHERE OF GAS

Nor are we through with the earth yet. Clinging to it, and enclosing everything, lithosphere and hydrosphere alike, is a blanket of gas. This we call the *air* or the *atmosphere*. (The latter word is from the Greek and means "a ball of vapor.")

The air is hardly ever considered a part of the earth, somehow, by the average person. Even scientists, when they try to determine the shape and the size of the earth, are concerned only with the lithosphere and hydrosphere. The diameter of the earth is always given from sea level on one side of the globe to sea level on the other. The air is not included.

Well, air is invisible and we're just not aware of it. We don't see it the way we see land or sea, so perhaps it is natural to leave it out. Of course, even primitive man could appreciate the power of winds, hurricanes and tornadoes. He invented terrifying storm gods to account for them. But as for quiet air, air on a perfectly calm day—there seemed no power in that.

The beginnings of the understanding of calm air and the power it contained came in 1643. An Italian physicist named Evangelista Torricelli (a pupil of Galileo) showed that air had weight. The pressure of its weight, pushing down, could balance a thirty-inch column of mercury and keep that mercury from pouring out of an upside-down tube. (In other words, he invented what we now call the *barometer*.)

In order for air to do this, Torricelli decided, there must be an *air pressure* of 14.7 pounds on every square inch of the earth. This weight, 14.7 pounds per square inch, is called *one atmosphere* of air pressure.

Can you imagine a column of air resting on one square inch of the earth's surface? That column extends upward for miles, reaching as far up as the atmosphere goes. All the air in that column weighs 14.7 pounds. This may not sound like much, perhaps, considering that we're dealing with miles upon miles of air. However, there's 14.7 pounds above each square inch of the earth's surface, and there are very many square inches to that surface.

The total mass of the atmosphere resting on all the square inches of the earth comes to 5,700,000,000,000,000 tons!

The Barometer

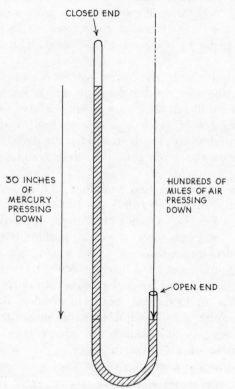

CLOSED END

30 INCHES
OF
MERCURY
PRESSING
DOWN

HUNDREDS OF
MILES OF AIR
PRESSING
DOWN

OPEN END

AIR PRESSURE = PRESSURE OF 30 INCHES OF MERCURY =
14.7 LBS./SQ. IN.

That is more than five and a half million billion tons.

This may seem hard to believe.

Hold your hand out and look at your palm. On every square inch of it, 14.7 pounds of air is resting. In fact, that weight of air is pushing on every square inch of your body. And yet you don't feel it, do you? Why is that?

The answer to this was given by a German physicist named Otto von Guericke, back in 1650, shortly after the barometer was invented. Von Guericke invented an *air pump*, a device which would suck air out of a metal sphere, leaving practically no air (a *vacuum*) inside.

Von Guericke then took two half spheres that fitted together smoothly. Through a valve in one of the hemispheres, he sucked the air out with his pump. Now there was a vacuum inside the fitted-together hemispheres. With no air inside, there was no air pressure inside. But there was air pressure outside, 14.7 pounds on every square inch of the two hemispheres. That air pressure held the two hemispheres firmly together.

Von Guericke showed this by tying each hemisphere to a team of horses and driving them apart before a large audience. The hemispheres held together. The horses could not pull them apart. Then he opened the valve and let air back into the hemispheres. Now there was air pressure inside the hemispheres, too. This canceled the air pressure on the outside. It was as though there were no pressure at all, and the two hemispheres fell apart by themselves.

If there were a vacuum within you, you would feel the air pressure, all right. In fact, the air pressure would kill you. But the substance of your body is at the same pressure as the outer air. It pushes out with just the force that air pushes in, and the two pressures are in balance. Like the hemispheres of von Guericke when air was let inside, there is no sign of any pressure at all, either way.

In fact, if you were wondering how we could stand air pressure, think of the creatures living at the bottom of the deepest part of the ocean, where miles of water weigh down upon them. There are many tons of water pressure to every square inch. But the same tons of pressure press outward from within those creatures. Deep-sea fish swim about comfortably, therefore, unaware of all the weight of water above them.

Another odd fact about gases, such as air, is that they can be made to have almost any density. The tiny particles that make up liquids and solids (called *molecules*) are practically in contact. If solids and liquids are put under pressure, it is difficult to push the molecules any farther together than they already are. Even under enormous pressure the density only goes up slightly. At the very center of the earth, iron is only two and one-half times as dense as it is on the surface.

The molecules of gases, on the other hand, are separated by distances many times their own diameter. (That is why gases have such low densities. After all, they are mostly empty space. The density of air is only 0.0013 gm/cc.) Even small pressures can push the molecules of air together by quite a large amount. It isn't very difficult to compress air to a hundred times its ordinary density.

Furthermore, the molecules of solids and liquids remain in contact even though there is no pressure on them at all. Solid iron can be made a trifle less dense than 7.86 gm/cc by heating it, but only a trifle. The molecules of a gas, however, can easily spread out to leave more and more space. A gas can therefore easily become *rarefied*. Air can be made a thousand times less dense than it normally is, or a million times less dense. There is no limit.

The lowest portion of the atmosphere, the part that is in contact with the surface of the earth, has to carry the weight of all the air above. This compresses the lowest portion of the air and makes that portion the densest air. Most human beings live in the particularly dense air that exists at sea level.

If you move up a mountain, however, you pass into parts of the air that are carrying less of a load. The higher you go the less dense the air becomes. People used to sea-level conditions find it difficult to get along in the high mountains until they become acclimated.

The air keeps on thinning and thinning until, above a height of, say, three miles, human beings could not live permanently. It keeps on thinning past that, too, thinner and thinner and incredibly thin. The atmosphere never comes to a sharp end, the way the lithosphere and the hydrosphere do. There is no boundary to the atmosphere; it just fades slowly away into the nothingness of outer space.

(If the air were as dense all the way up as it is on the earth's surface, the atmosphere would be only five miles high. The highest mountains would be sticking up out of it.)

Perhaps it is just as well, then, that the atmosphere isn't included in considering the size and shape of the earth. Without a real surface, the atmosphere would confuse things terribly.

As we travel up a mountain, the air pressure drops because we leave some of the air below us as we climb upward. The weight of the portion of the air that is still above us becomes less and less as we climb.

At a height of three and one-half miles, say at the top of Mt. Elbruz in the Caucasus (the highest mountain in Europe), half the atmosphere is below. The air pressure is down to 7.4 pounds per square inch (0.5 atmosphere).

At the top of Mt. Everest, which is 5½ miles high and the highest peak on the earth, the air pressure is 4.5 pounds per square inch (0.3 atmosphere).

Airplanes and balloons go higher still, of course, and have reached as high as twenty-six miles above Earth's surface.

At that height, air pressure is only about an ounce per square inch. More than ninety-nine per cent of the atmosphere is below. However, the remaining one per cent stretches thinly upward for hundreds of miles more.

(Perhaps you might be wondering why the atmosphere isn't very thin at the equator, which is at the top of the equatorial bulge. The air doesn't slide down to the poles any more than the ocean does, however. The centrifugal force that forms the bulge in the first place also lifts the ocean and atmosphere with the crust and keeps them in place.)

THE DIVISIONS OF AIR

The lowest and the thickest part of the atmosphere is where all our familiar weather takes place. It contains all the clouds and storms. It contains the wind movements. It is the part of the air that is always changing to make our weather patterns. For this reason it is called the *troposphere*. ("Tropo-" comes from a Greek word meaning "change.")

The troposphere is only six to ten miles high altogether (the exact height varies with latitude and with season) but it contains at least two-thirds of the total mass of the atmosphere. The temperature drops steadily as we go higher in the troposphere; that is why high mountain peaks are permanently covered with snow. Several miles up, the temperature is below the freezing point of water even in the summer. At the top of the troposphere the temperature has sunk to 70 degrees below zero Fahrenheit.

During World War II, planes flying near the top of the troposphere found strong winds present. That is how it was discovered that there are two currents of air circling the earth from east to west at a height of five to ten miles. One is in the northern hemisphere and one in the southern, both about halfway between the equator and the pole. They travel at velocities of from one hundred to five hundred miles an hour. These are the *jet streams,* and they are now thought to be responsible for much of the general weather pattern on the earth.

In the 1930's stretches of air above the troposphere were studied by balloons carrying instruments. In the 1950's rockets and satellites have sent down information from heights balloons could not reach.

That is how we know, for instance, that above the troposphere is a region of thin air where the temperature does not change. It remains at 70 below throughout. There are neither clouds nor weather changes here. Because of this, the air in that region is quietly spread out in a series of undisturbed layers, and this region is called the *stratosphere.* ("Strato-" comes from a Greek word meaning "layer.") The boundary between the troposphere and the stratosphere is the *tropopause.*

At a height of about thirty miles, the temperature starts rising again. Somewhere between that point and a height of fifty miles, the stratosphere comes to an end.

Although the air in the stratosphere is thin, it is important to us. There are deadly radiations in space, originating in the sun and elsewhere. One of these is ultraviolet light, and that is absorbed in the stratosphere. The oxygen in the stratosphere absorbs it and is converted in the process to an active form of oxygen called *ozone.* The layer of ozone about fifteen miles high in the air (sometimes called the *ozonosphere*) is what stands between us and a quick death by over exposure to ultraviolet. (Even so, enough ultraviolet gets through to sunburn light-skinned human beings and to cause considerable discomfort at times.)

Above the stratosphere, what thin wisps of air still remain are exposed to the full force of various radiations—such as that of the *cosmic rays,* which are composed of very energetic particles. These speeding particles strike air molecules, knocking small bits off. What is left of the molecules carry electric charges and are called *ions*. The region of the atmosphere above the stratosphere is therefore called the *ionosphere*.

Molecules struck by cosmic rays give rise to various new particles (called *secondary radiation*) which shoot off in all directions. Some of this secondary radiation and even some of the original cosmic rays reach the very surface of the earth. However, fortunately for us, the upper reaches of air do take care of the worst of it.

The ions in the ionosphere can reflect radio waves of the type that are used in ordinary radio broadcasts. This is what makes long-distance radio signaling possible. If the reflection did not take place, these radio waves would just travel in straight lines away from the earth. (Very short-wave radio waves, such as those used in television, are not reflected. They pierce the ionosphere and travel on. That is why long-distance television is rather difficult to arrange. Of course, we are now putting large balloons into space. The first of these, launched in July 1960, was called Echo I. These can reflect short-wave radio waves and could revolutionize television transmission and all sorts of electronic communications.)

This was discovered in 1902, by two different physicists, the Englishman Oliver Heaviside and the American Arthur E. Kennelly. A reflecting layer of ions at a height of about fifty miles above the earth's surface is called the *Kennelly-Heaviside layer,* in their honor.

It is in the ionosphere, too, that most meteors come to their end. There the many millions of tiny particles of pinhead size or smaller, that strike the atmosphere, are completely vaporized. Meteor trails have been detected at heights of from fifty to one hundred miles, so that there is still air enough at those heights to supply sufficient friction to destroy small meteors.

Layers of the Atmosphere

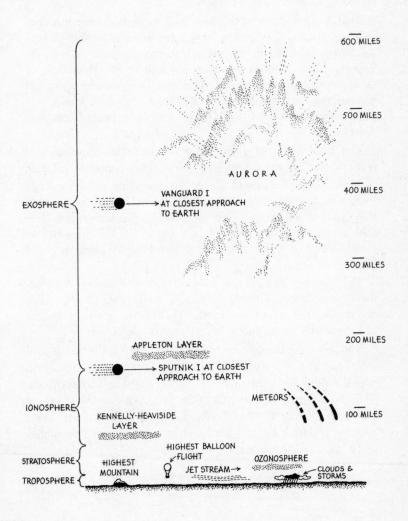

Beyond a hundred miles above the surface of the earth, there is not enough air to bother meteors, but there is still some air. Reflecting layers of ions have been detected by the English physicist, Edward V. Appleton, at heights of one hundred and fifty to two hundred miles. These are now referred to as the *Appleton layers.*

Artificial satellites which approach to within two hundred miles of the earth's surface have been sent into orbit around the earth. Wisps of air present there are not enough to vaporize these satellites, but are enough to absorb a little of their energy of movement. The satellites slowly spiral in toward the earth. Eventually they come in close enough to enter the ionosphere, and there they are heated up and destroyed.

The final trace of atmosphere beyond the hundred-mile level is called the *exosphere.* How high does it extend?

Well, the thin wisps of air in the exosphere absorb energy from tiny particles shot into it by the sun, and as a result they sometimes glow. This happens particularly after certain types of storms have taken place on the sun—storms which shoot a great many particles (called *electrons*) out into space.

The glowing of the exosphere is called the *aurora.* Astronomers have detected faint auroras up to heights of 680 miles above the surface of the earth. That is the greatest height at which any atmospheric effect can be detected.

Now let's go back to our six-foot model of the earth and see what the atmosphere looks like. Clinging to the earth model would be a thin wisp of vapor about 1/12 inch thick. That is the troposphere. Outside that, with a thickness of about 1/3 inch, is the stratosphere. The ionosphere adds another 1/2 inch or so. Finally, stretching out for five inches more, is the exosphere.

Can there be anything outside the exosphere that belongs to our planet and can be considered part of it?

The answer is yes, but no one knew anything about it till 1958. To explain, I must first talk about magnetism.

FIVE

OUTSIDE THE AIR

THE LINES OF FORCE

About 2,500 years ago, a Greek shepherd near the city of Magnesia in Asia Minor is supposed to have come across a black rock which attracted the iron tip of his staff. Other such rocks were also found, and the Greek philosopher Thales called them "magnes" after the city near which they were first found. From this comes our own word *magnet*.

If a piece of steel or iron is stroked by one of these magnetic rocks, it becomes magnetized, too. The new magnet can now attract iron or steel just as the original rock did.

Now suppose a piece of magnetized steel is placed on a small sheet of cork and set afloat in a pan of water. The cork will turn until one end is facing north. If it is turned away, it will swing and turn back.

The Chinese are supposed to have discovered this a thousand years ago. They mounted such a needle so that it could swing freely in a horizontal direction. On shipboard such a *magnetic compass* always gave the direction of north, even during cloudy weather, when sun and stars were not visible.

The first West European to write about magnets and describe how to build a compass was a French engineer named Peter Peregrinus. Between 1266 and 1269, he studied magnets and discovered that each one had two points where the magnetic force seemed most concentrated. In a magnetized needle, the poles were at the two tips. These were the *magnetic poles*. One of these poles always pointed toward the north; this was the *north magnetic pole*. The other, which always pointed south, was the *south magnetic pole*.

If two magnetized needles are brought close together, the two north magnetic poles push each other away. So do the two south magnetic poles. If the north magnetic pole of one were brought near the south magnetic pole of the other, however, there would be an attraction. Like poles repel; unlike poles attract.

It was the compass that made long sea voyages practical. Without it, ships clung to shore to avoid getting lost in the vast empty stretches of ocean. With a compass, ships could afford to be bolder. Columbus probably would not have made his trip without a compass; so you see it was a world-shaking invention.

Now a magnet did more than just point north. If a magnetized needle were held so that it could swing freely up and down, the north magnetic pole always dipped down toward the ground. Not straight down, but at a certain definite angle. This is called *magnetic dip*.

Why should all this be? In England, the physician to Queen Elizabeth I, William Gilbert, wondered. He spent his spare time experimenting with magnets, and in 1600 he published a book on them. He described how he had prepared a magnet in the shape of a rather large sphere and brought a compass needle near it. The needle acted toward the magnetic sphere just as it acted toward the earth. The north magnetic pole of the needle pointed toward the north of the globe. In the northern hemisphere of the globe it dipped toward the ground; in the southern hemisphere, the north magnetic pole angled up and the south magnetic pole dipped.

Gilbert decided that the earth itself is a huge magnet, and so it indeed seems to be.

Scientists still don't know exactly why the earth should be a magnet. When it turned out that the earth had an iron core, it seemed natural to suppose that the core was magnetic. However, the iron core is too hot to be magnetic. (If a magnet is heated strongly, it loses all its magnetism, and the magnetism does not come back with cooling, either.) The most recent theory is that the rotation of the earth sets up electric currents in the iron core and that these currents give rise to the magnetism.

As a magnet, the earth ought to have poles just as any other magnet has. It does. There are two magnetic poles on earth. One is at the far northern tip of Canada, near the Boothia Peninsula. It is nearly a thousand miles away from the geographic north pole. A compass needle in that spot, if free to swing in any direction, would turn so that the north magnetic pole would point straight down.

The other pole is at the rim of Antarctica, near the Ross Sea, nearly a thousand miles from the geographic south pole.

The two magnetic poles are not quite opposite each other. A line drawn through the earth from one magnetic pole to the other (such a line is called the *magnetic axis*) would not pass through the center of the earth.

Because the magnetic poles aren't exactly at the geographic poles, a compass needle doesn't point exactly north. What's more, as you move east or west, the compass needle changes direction somewhat (partly becuase of various local conditions). This difference between magnetic north and true north is called *magnetic variation* or *magnetic declination*. Nowadays there are elaborate charts giving the exact magnetic variation for practically every spot on Earth. When Columbus sailed on his great voyage, though, changing magnetic variation was noticed for the first time. Columbus was careful to keep this from his men, lest he frighten them and drive them to mutiny.

Now suppose you had a bar of magnetized steel under a piece of paper. Over the paper you scatter some iron filings (tiny slivers of iron). If you tapped the paper, the filings would vibrate and take up definite positions in the form of curved lines running from one of the magnetic poles to the other.

This may have first been done by Peter Peregrinus, but it was a much later English scientist named Michael Faraday who really thought this matter out, about 1820.

He suggested that a magnet spread its influence through nearby space in what he called a *magnetic field*. This field behaved as though it were made up of *magnetic lines of force* (as Faraday called them), which curved from one

The Earth As a Magnet

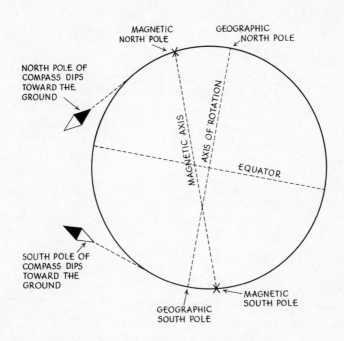

pole to the other. Iron filings placed over a magnet turned themselves so as to lie along the lines of force. So did a compass needle.

Now if the earth is a large magnet, it, too, must have magnetic lines of force all about it. These must lead from magnetic pole to magnetic pole, curving for many thousands of miles out into space. The compass needle on Earth points along those lines of force. The north magnetic pole of the compass points north and toward the ground in the northern hemisphere; north and toward the sky in the southern hemisphere, following those lines of force.

Magnetic Lines of Force

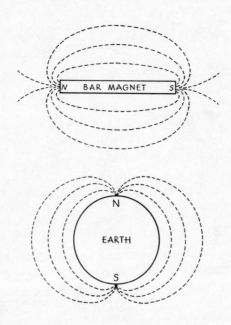

TURNED BY THE LINES

How is the earth affected by its magnetic field?

Well, the earth is continually being bombarded by tiny particles, far tinier than atoms, which carry electric charges. I mentioned two varieties of these in the previous chapter. There are cosmic rays, which are comparatively massive particles; and electrons, which are much lighter particles.

Now electric charges are affected by magnetic fields. A tiny particle carrying an electric charge tends to be bent out of its path if it moves across magnetic lines of force.

As the cosmic ray particles approach the earth, for instance, they are bent to one side and are forced to move toward the magnetic poles. The cosmic rays are so energetic that many force their way across the lines of force without being turned much, so that all parts of the earth are struck. However, the equatorial regions get less than the rest of the earth. Cosmic-ray bombardment gets more intense as you go toward the north or south from the equator. It is, in fact, twice as intense in the Arctic and Antarctic as at the equator.

(As a matter of fact, it was this variation north and south that gave scientists the hint that cosmic rays were composed of charged particles. When cosmic rays were first discovered, it was thought they were radiation like light and x-rays. If that had been so, however, they would not have been affected by Earth's magnetic field.)

Electrons behave as do the cosmic rays. Being lighter, however, speeding electrons are bent out of their path to a far greater extent than are cosmic rays. Practically none of them strike the equatorial regions and almost all hit the atmosphere in the far north and south.

As I said in the previous chapter, when electrons strike the exosphere, an aurora results. Because of Earth's magnetism, the aurora occurs only in the north and south, never in tropical regions. That is why, in the northern hemisphere, people speak of the *Aurora Borealis* ("Aurora of the North") or the *Northern Lights*. In the southern hemisphere there is the *Aurora Australis* ("Aurora of the South") or the *Southern Lights*.

The electrons, as I have said, originate from the sun. There are disturbances in the hot surface of the sun which result in a particularly violent spray of electrons. When some of these strike the earth's exosphere, they bring about unusually bright and widespread aurorae. At these times, people living in the temperate zones may be treated to a display. (I have seen two such displays, one from New York in 1938, and one from Boston in 1958. They are wonderful.)

Although beautiful, aurorae can be troublesome, too. As the electrons smash into the upper atmosphere, they not only create a glow, they also disturb the ionized layers in the ionosphere. During such a *magnetic storm*, radio and television, which depend on radio waves bouncing off layers in the ionosphere, are upset. During the 1958 auroral display, for instance, I was watching television (when I wasn't looking at the aurora) and my set kept switching channels without my touching a knob.

THE RADIATION BELTS

This behavior of cosmic rays and electrons has been known for something like thirty years. But once mankind started sending satellites around the earth, something new turned up.

When Explorer I was sent up by the United States Army on January 31, 1958, it had instruments that reacted to particles striking it. The radio signal sent back varied according to the number of particles that struck. In this way, information was received about the amount of radiation and about charged particles out there in space.

Even at the nearest point in its orbit to the earth's surface,

Explorer I was still well out into the exosphere. Consequently, scientists were not surprised when it registered more radiation than existed on the surface of the earth. After all, it was picking up particles before the atmosphere had had a chance to absorb them and thin them out.

However, in those parts of its orbit where Explorer I was farthest from the earth, where it was well beyond the limits even of the exosphere, it registered practically no particles at all. That was strange. Scientists had expected it would register still more at the high point of the orbit than at the low point.

It was James A. Van Allen of the State University of Iowa, the man in charge of studying the radiation data, who suggested an explanation. There was radiation at the high point, he said, but so much more radiation than expected that the instruments supposed to pick it up couldn't handle it. The radiation counters had been put out of action. (That's as though a bright flash of light had blinded you so that you couldn't see anything.)

On July 26, 1958, Explorer IV was sent up with instruments specially designed to handle a lot of radiation. The counters were covered with lead so that most of the particles would be absorbed. (That's like wearing dark glasses for protection against bright flashes of light.)

Van Allen's suggestion turned out to be correct. From the particles that managed to get through the lead shields, it seemed that there was far more radiation in space near Earth than had been expected.

Then, on October 11, 1958, a rocket (Pioneer II) was shot almost to the moon and information about the radiation and charged particles even farther out from the earth was obtained.

It turned out that there are two belts of charged particles

circling the earth. In honor of the discoverer, they are called the *Van Allen radiation belts.*

These belts arise because electrons can be trapped by the magnetic lines of force. They spiral back and forth along the lines from north magnetic pole to south magnetic pole. Some are continually leaking down to the earth to cause aurorae, but large amounts accumulate and are always present in space.

The inner radiation belt surrounds the earth at a height of between 1,500 and 3,000 miles above the surface. The outer belt surrounds it at a height of between 8,000 and 12,000 miles. The electrons of the inner belt may have been sucked up out of the earth's atmosphere, having been formed there when cosmic rays hit the atoms of the upper air. The electrons of the outer belt may come directly from the sun.

Both belts follow the magnetic lines of force and are thickest in the equatorial regions where the lines are farthest from the earth's surface and farthest apart. Near the magnetic poles, the lines draw together and approach the surface of the earth. There the belts are thinnest and even fade out. There is a "funnel" in the Arctic and the Antarctic that is fairly free of radiation. (The satellite, Explorer VI, which was launched by the United States on August 7, 1959, detected a small third belt closer to the earth than either of the others. It is about 1,000 miles above the surface of the planet.)

Charged particles striking the metal of a space ship will result in a flood of x-rays that could be damaging, or even fatal, to the men inside. For that reason the discovery of the Van Allen radiation belts worried people who were hoping for space flight soon.

However, there are still the "funnels" in the north and south. It may mean that manned space ships will have to shoot up from Greenland or from Antarctica, but at least they can get up somehow. Meanwhile, too, there is the gap between the belts. Within that gap manned space stations can circle the earth around the equator in reasonable safety.

The man who first suggested that electrons might not only be turned by the lines of force, but actually be trapped by them, was Nicholas Christofilos, a Greek engineer now at the University of California. This trapping is therefore called the *Christofilos effect*.

In late 1958, American scientists decided to test whether the Christofilos effect really existed. They rocketed atomic bombs high up above the surface of the earth and exploded them at a height of three hundred miles. (This was called "Project Argus.")

The Van Allen Radiation Belts

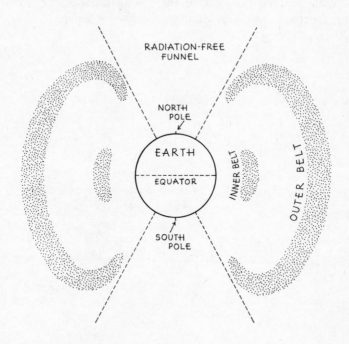

The exploding bombs released charged particles which then behaved exactly as Christofilos had predicted. They were trapped along the lines of force. What's more, those that managed to get far enough within the atmosphere to the north and south set up a small magnetic storm.

If we return to our six-foot model globe again, the inner Van Allen radiation belt circles the earth's equator like a doughnut. The doughnut would be about one and one-half feet thick and would be separated from the earth by a distance of about one foot.

The outer belt would be a much larger doughnut bulging outward something like a tubeless rubber tire. It would be six feet from the model and would be about three feet thick.

And beyond the radiation belts?

Well, nothing to speak of for a long distance. Then, far out in space, we meet another world—the moon.

SIX

THE NEARNESS OF "NEAREST"

THE RACING MOON

The moon has always been especially admired by mankind. It and the sun are the only two heavenly bodies that are more than mere points of light. The sun is far more spectacular, but it is too bright to look at. In times of heat and drought, it can even be deadly.

But the moon's soft rays hurt no one, and give light in the darkness. It can be looked at in comfort. Besides, its shape is always changing, and that makes it even more interesting. Sometimes it is a full circle of light, sometimes half, sometimes a curving crescent.

Early man made use of this changing shape of the moon to work out a calendar. The influence of the moon still shows up in our modern calendar, even though today we base it on the sun. For instance, the word "month" comes from "moon."*

The early astronomers in Babylonia and Egypt (even before the days of the Greeks) discovered something else of particular interest in connection with the moon. This came about through a study of its motions.

You see, the stars always form the same pattern in the sky. True, they seem to move about the earth from east

---

*If you are interested in the way in which the calendar was devised, and its connection with the moon, you will find the details in my book *The Clock We Live On*, Abelard-Schuman, 1959.

to west, making a complete circle in a day (thanks to the earth's rotation) but they all move together. The stars form a steady background, therefore, and against this the motions of other bodies can be studied.

For instance, there are five particularly bright starlike objects in the sky, which we call Mercury, Venus, Mars, Jupiter and Saturn. These change positions in comparison to the stars. They may be just east of a particular star one night, and then be found a bit farther to the east of it the next night, farther still the next night, and so on.

These wandering objects are called *planets,* from a Greek word meaning "wandering." If the position of each planet is observed at different times, it can be seen to move completely around the sky. The line of its movement makes a rather complicated pattern against the starry background, however, and is not a simple circle. The sun and the moon also move against the background of the stars (in a simpler pattern). To the ancients, these were considered planets also.

It was from a study of these movements, by the way, that astronomers slowly worked out the structure of the Solar System.*

Each planet takes a particular time to move completely around the sky. For instance, Saturn takes 29 years to move once around. Jupiter only takes twelve years, and the sun a single year. The ancient astronomers decided that the longer it takes a planet to move around the sky, the greater the distance it has to cover, and the farther it is from the earth. (If you are running around a tree, it will take you longer to run once around if you are following a circle that is one hundred feet from the tree, than if you are following one that is ten feet from it.)

*How this was done is explained in detail in my book *The Kingdom of the Sun,* Abelard-Schuman, 1959.

Of all the heavenly bodies, the moon takes the least time to make a circuit of the sky against the background of the stars. It does this in just a little over twenty-seven days. (That is what makes a month, by the way; the circuit of the moon around the sky.)

For this reason, even the Babylonian and Egyptian astronomers decided that the moon was of particular interest to us because it is our neighbor. Of all the heavenly bodies, the moon is nearest to the earth.

Of course, they had no idea of how near "nearest" was. It was the Greeks who first tried to find out how far away the moon was in actual distance.

But how is this done? We can't very well stretch a tape measure from here to the moon. Well, let's see—

Measuring by Eye-Blink

The closer an object is, the larger it appears. So, to begin with, how large does the moon appear?

It's no use saying it looks a foot across or three inches across, because we can't hold a ruler against it to see.

Instead, it must be measured by angles.

Suppose you are looking at an object and imaginary lines are drawn from opposite ends of the object to your eye. The two lines form an angle at your eye; the larger that angle, the larger the object appears. Therefore, you can measure the apparent size of an object by the size of the angle it makes (or *subtends*) at your eye.

It frequently happens in such cases that the angle is less than one degree. It is usual, then, to divide each degree into sixty equal subdivisions called *minutes of arc*, and each minute into sixty *seconds of arc*.

(The ancient Babylonians who first decided to divide a complete circle into 360 degrees also first used divisions by sixty to set up minutes and seconds. The Greeks adopted the notion and it has been used ever since. We have a similar inheritance from the Babylonians in our system of telling time. Each hour is divided into sixty minutes, and each minute into sixty seconds.)

It turns out that the angle formed by lines drawn from opposite sides of the full moon to the eye comes to just a trifle over half a degree. Half a degree is equal to thirty minutes. The angular size of the moon is thirty-one minutes and five seconds, on the average.

The angular size, all by itself, however, doesn't tell us the real size. Any particular object will assume a different angular size according to its distance from the eye.

In other words, an object of a particular size will subtend a certain angle if held at a given distance. If the distance increases, the angle subtended decreases (and the object looks smaller). That is common sense. If the distance decreases, the angle subtended increases, and the object looks larger.

There is a branch of mathematics called *trigonometry* that deals with just this matter. Ways have been worked out to measure the angle subtended, or the distance, or the size of an object. If any two of these are known, the third

Angles and Distances

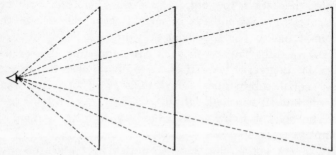

THE FURTHER THE OBJECT, THE SMALLER THE SUBTENDED ANGLE

can be calculated. If you know the size of an object and its distance from your eye, you can calculate the angle it will subtend. From the angle it subtends and its distance, if both are known, you can calculate its size. From the angle it subtends and its size, you can calculate its distance.

For instance, using trigonometry, I can say that a yardstick held up six feet from the eye will take up an angle of 28 degrees and 6 minutes. Knowing the size of the yardstick, and its distance, you see, I can calculate the angle it will subtend. If the distance is increased to twenty feet, the angle it subtends is decreased to 8 degrees and 35 minutes. If the distance is increased farther to 330 feet, the angle decreases to 31 minutes, just the angular width of the moon.

A yardstick held 330 feet away, then, if placed between the eye and the full moon, would seem to stretch from one side of the moon just to the other. Does that mean the moon, too, is a yard across and 330 feet away?

Not necessarily. If you took a stick that was four yards long and held it a quarter of a mile away, it, too, would subtend an angle of 31 minutes. Or if you took a dime and held it 6 feet away from your eye, it would subtend an angle of 31 minutes.

Well, then, does this mean that the moon is four yards wide and a quarter of a mile away? Or does it mean that it is the size of a dime and 6 feet away?

You simply can't tell just from knowing the angle an object subtends. That is only one piece of information, and trigonometry requires two. If you knew the moon's distance as well as the angle it subtends, you could calculate its real size. Or if you knew the size as well as the angle, you could calculate its distance. Knowing only the angle doesn't help you.

Is there a way out? Yes, fortunately, there is.

Hold your finger about six inches before your face, close

your right eye and look at it with the left. You will notice
that the finger is in a certain position against the background.
It is near a particular piece of furniture, perhaps, if you are
indoors, or near a particular tree or part of a building if you
are outdoors.

Now don't move your finger, just open your right eye and
close your left. Notice how your finger seems to have jumped
and changed position against the background? That is because
you are now looking at it from another position, since the
pupil of your right eye is a few inches from that of your left
eye.

Next, repeat the process, but this time hold your finger
out as far as your arm will reach. The finger still changes
position as you switch eyes, but do you notice that the
change is much smaller?

This apparent motion of a near object against a distant
background, when the near object is looked at from different
positions, is referred to as *parallactic displacement*. The
amount by which an object seems to move in this way is
its *parallax*.

Trigonometry can be used to determine the distance of
an object by the amount of its parallax. Consider your finger.
The distance it was displaced when you switched eyes can
be measured as an angle. (This angle is formed by a line
from each eye to the object.) The distance between your
eyes can be measured; this is called the *baseline*.

If you can measure the angle of parallax and the size
of the baseline, you have two pieces of knowledge—angle
and size. Trigonometry will now give you the distance of
your finger from your eye, which is the third piece of
knowledge.

The farther an object is from your eyes, the smaller its
parallax. Suppose you are looking at a telephone pole a
thousand feet away and comparing its position with that

of a particular spot on the horizon. If you close first your right eye and then your left, there will be parallactic displacement. However, the amount will be tiny indeed, only two minutes of arc. That would scarcely be enough to work with, unless you were using special instruments.

You can make things simpler by increasing the size of the baseline. Instead of standing in one place and just switching from eye to eye, you can move about. You can sight the telephone pole against the horizon from one spot. Then you can move fifty feet to one side and sight again. Now the parallax will be nearly 3 degrees, and very easy to measure. With a parallax of 3 degrees and a baseline of fifty feet, trigonometry will tell you that the telephone pole is 1,000 feet away.

But what about the moon?

It is much farther away than even the telephone pole, so you need a baseline much longer than fifty feet. Suppose the moon is observed from two observatories at the same time; one in Los Angeles, California, and one in Baghdad, Iraq. That would give a baseline of about 7,800 miles in length (measuring straight through the earth, not along the curve of its surface.)

When the position of the moon is compared with stars in the same region of the sky, the two observatories will be found to be 1 degree 50 minutes apart. From the parallax (angle) and the length of the baseline (size), it is now possible to calculate how far the moon is from the earth (distance). By use of trigonometry, the angle and size, if known, can be used to give the distance.

Naturally, the moon, as the closest of the heavenly bodies, shows the largest parallax. Actually, I should put that in reverse. It has been found to have the largest parallax, and so we now know that the ancient astronomers were correct when they decided it was our nearest neighbor in space because it seemed to move so quickly.

The parallax is so easy to measure, in fact, even without a telescope, that the moon was the one object in the sky whose distance was known pretty well to some of the later Greek astronomers.

Based on the best modern measurements, the distance of the moon from the earth turns out to be, on the average, 238,857 miles. This is a large distance, but not impossibly large. It is only a trifle more than 9 times the distance about the earth. Many a man has driven his automobile that distance and more in his lifetime.

Parallax and Distance

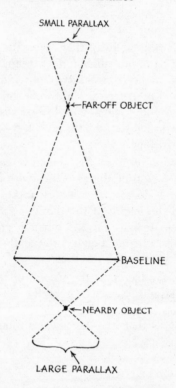

SMALL PARALLAX

FAR-OFF OBJECT

BASELINE

NEARBY OBJECT

LARGE PARALLAX

COMPARING THE NEIGHBORS

Once the distance of the moon is known, along with its angular size, it is easy to calculate its real size by trigonometry. The moon turns out to have a diameter of 2,160 miles.

This means that if we go back once more to our six-foot model of the earth, the moon is another globe, not quite twenty inches (or 1 2/3 feet, if you prefer) in diameter. Its distance from the six-foot model would be 180 feet, or nearly 3/4 of a city block.

The diameter of the moon is more than one-quarter the diameter of the earth. To be more exact, the moon's diameter is 0.273 of the earth's diameter. Or if you would like it the other way around, the earth's diameter is 3.67 times the diameter of the moon.

Often someone may say "the moon is a quarter the size of the earth," meaning the diameter. This, however, gives a false notion of the moon's size.

When we talk about the size of a country, we are usually referring to its surface area. In the same way, when man lands on the moon, he will be interested in its surface area.

But the surface of two spheres is in proportion to the square of their diameters. For instance if sphere A has twice the diameter of sphere B, it has 2 x 2 or 4 times the surface area. If sphere A has five times the diameter of sphere B, it has 5 x 5 or 25 times the surface area; and so on.

I have just said that the earth has 3.67 times the diameter of the moon. Therefore the earth has 3.67 x 3.67 or 13.5 times the surface area. Since the surface area of the earth is just about 197,000,000 square miles, the surface area of the moon must be 14,600,000 square miles. This is about twelve per cent less than the area of North and South America combined. In other words, the first man who lands on the moon will be on a world of surface somewhat smaller than the surface of the continents discovered by Columbus.

Or, to put it still another way, the surface area of the moon is just about four times as great as that of the United States.

Maybe this is less impressive than to say that the moon is "one quarter the size" of the earth. If so, there is even a bigger disappointment when we consider volume. The volume of two spheres is in proportion to the cube of their diameters. For instance, if sphere A has twice the diameter of sphere B, it has 2 x 2 x 2 or eight times the volume. If sphere A has five times the diameter of sphere B, it has 5 x 5 x 5 or 125 times the volume, and so on.

Since the earth's diameter is 3.67 times that of the moon, the earth's volume must be 3.67 x 3.67 x 3.67, or just about fifty times the volume of the moon. At the beginning of Chapter 3, I said the earth had a volume of 260,000,000,000 cubic miles. The volume of the moon is only 5,260,000,000 cubic miles.

This is still quite a bit, of course. But the fact remains that, if the earth were hollow, it would take fifty moons (squashed in tightly) to fill it up.

The Earth and the Moon Compared

Does this seem to you to make the moon appear to be a tiny world? Its volume is only 1/50 (or two per cent) that of the earth.

Well, if you feel the moon is beneath your notice, consider that there isn't another planet in the whole Solar System which has a moon anywhere near as large in comparison with itself. The largest moon of the planet Saturn has only 1/15,000 the volume of Saturn. The largest moon of the planet Jupiter has only 1/20,000 the volume of Jupiter.

Compared with that, a figure like 1/50 seems giant-size.

In fact, the earth and the moon are so nearly alike in size (compared to other planets and their moons) that they are the nearest thing in the Solar System to a double planet. That is why I have chosen the title *The Double Planet* for this book.

SEVEN

THE CIRCLINGS OF THE WORLDS

THE UNEVEN PATH

The ancients believed that the earth was the center of the universe and that the moon, the sun and all the planets revolved about the earth. Two Greek astronomers, Hipparchus and Ptolemy, worked this out in complete mathematical detail. This notion is referred to as the *geocentric system* ("earth-centered") or, in honor of Ptolemy, the *Ptolemaic system*.

The Ptolemaic system dominated astronomical thinking until the 1500's. Then Copernicus popularized the theory that the earth and all the planets revolved about the sun. This is the *heliocentric system* ("sun-centered") or the *Copernican system*.

In passing from the Ptolemaic system to the Copernican system, the earth, however, was not shorn of every last scrap of its glory. To be sure, men no longer thought the sun revolved about it, or any of the distant planets. But one faithful heavenly body remained to us.

Even after Copernicus had shown the sun to be the center of the Solar System, we still kept the moon. It is the only heavenly body that really does circle the earth.

The moon makes one complete *revolution* about the earth in 27 days 7 hours 43 minutes 11.5 seconds. This is called the *sidereal month*. ("Sidereal" comes from a Latin word meaning "star," because the time of the moon's revolution is determined by observing its motions against the starry background.)

But in one way, the ancient system was changed even as regards the moon. That one way is in connection with the exact path followed by the moon as it circles the earth. Ptolemy, and Copernicus, too, for that matter, thought that all the heavenly bodies moved in perfect circles, so that the moon, for instance, moved in a perfect circle about the earth.

This raised some difficulties. For one thing, the moon didn't always travel at the same speed. During one half of the month, it moved a trifle more quickly than average, and during the other half a trifle more slowly.

Again, there was the fact that the moon did not always appear to be the same size. In the half of the month in which it was traveling at a faster than normal rate, it also seemed a bit larger than normal. In the other half, when it was moving more slowly, it seemed a bit smaller.

This may surprise you, since you have probably never noticed any particular change in the moon's size. You see, it's a very small change and only careful measurement will show it.

In the previous chapter I said that the moon's apparent diameter was 31 minutes and 5 seconds, but I added "on the average." Careful measurement shows that sometimes the moon is as large as 33 minutes and 30 seconds. Sometimes it is as small as 29 minutes and 21 seconds.

Naturally, no one thinks the moon expands and contracts like an accordion. The logical explanation is that the moon is closer to the earth during one half of the month, and then seems to be larger and to move faster. It is more distant from the earth the other half of the month, and then seems to be smaller and to move more slowly.

In fact, accurate modern measurements of the moon's apparent size, and the use of trigonometry, show that the moon can be as close as 221,463 miles to the earth at times. It can also be as far as 252,710 miles at other times. The distance I gave in the previous chapter, 238,857, is only an average, as I said at the time.

The ancients were aware of the unevennesses in the moon's path and suspected it was closer to the earth at some times and farther at other times. But if the moon's path were a perfect circle, why should this be? All points on the circumference of a circle should be an equal distance from the center.

They tried a number of techniques to get out of this mess. They tried to make the moon's path fit the combination of a number of different perfect spheres, instead of fitting just one. They tried to have the moon revolve about a center that wasn't exactly at the center of the earth, but a little to one side. None of these ways out was satisfactory.

Even Copernicus had nothing better to offer.

Then, in 1609, more than sixty years after the death of Copernicus, a German astronomer named Johann Kepler first suggested that circles be abandoned. He showed that the motions of heavenly bodies were more easily explained by supposing they moved in ellipses. (Do you remember that we ran across ellipses before, when talking about measuring the degree along a meridian, at the end of Chapter 2?)

Well, then, it is time to look more closely at what an ellipse is like, before proceeding farther.

THE FLATTENED CURVE

An ellipse is a closed curve that looks like a flattened circle. If you were to draw lines across an ellipse in different directions from one point on the curve to another, you would find that one particular line was the longest you could draw. This would be the *major axis* of the ellipse. The midpoint of that line is the *center* of the ellipse.

On the major axis are two special points called *foci* (the singular form is *focus*). One focus is a certain distance to one side of the center and the other focus is at the same distance to the other side of the center.

What makes these special points so special? Well, suppose you draw a straight line from one focus to any point on the circumference of a particular ellipse (any point at all). Next draw a second straight line from the other focus to the same point on the circumference. No matter what point on the circumference you have chosen, the sum of those two lines you have drawn is always the same and always equal to the length of the major axis. This will not happen for any two points in the ellipse other than the foci.

The positions of the foci in a particular ellipse depend on the shape of that ellipse. If the ellipse is just a slightly flattened circle, then the two foci are very close to the center. (In fact, in a perfect circle, you might suppose that the two foci have come so close to the center that all three points have merged into one.) If, on the other hand, the ellipse is greatly flattened into a kind of cigar shape, the foci are far from the center and are near the two ends of the major axis.

One way of describing the type of ellipse being handled is to divide the distance between the foci by the length of the major axis. The greater the distance between the foci, the farther they are from the center of the ellipse; the more "out of center" they are. The distance between the foci divided by the length of the major axis is therefore called the *eccentricity* of the ellipse, from Greek words meaning "out of center."

In a circle, the two foci coincide at the center, so the distance between them is zero. The major axis of a circle is its diameter, and zero divided by the diameter is still zero. Consequently, the eccentricity of a circle is zero.

In a very flattened cigar-shaped ellipse, the foci are so far apart that the distance between them is almost equal to the length of the major axis. Therefore, dividing the first by the second gives an answer that is almost 1.

Thus, the eccentricity of an ellipse can vary from practically 0 to practically 1. The smaller the eccentricity is, the closer to a circle the ellipse appears in shape. The larger the eccentricity is, the more cigar-shaped the ellipse is.

Astronomers carefully observe the motion of the moon against the stars and calculate an ellipse that will best fit its line of motion. When this is done, it turns out that the moon moves about the earth in an ellipse that has an eccentricity of 0.055. (An ellipse with such a low eccentricity looks like a circle, at a casual glance.)

The major axis of the moon's ellipse is about 475,000 miles long. The distance between the foci of that ellipse is 475,000 x 0.055, or a little over 26,000 miles.

Now here's another interesting thing about the foci. Kepler also showed, back in 1609, that when one heavenly body

Ellipses

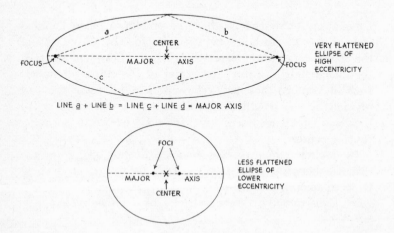

LINE a + LINE b = LINE c + LINE d = MAJOR AXIS

moved about another, the central body was not at the center of the ellipse but at one of the foci. The center of the ellipse and the other focus were empty.

In other words, when the moon moves about the earth in an ellipse, the earth is located at one of the foci of that ellipse. When the moon is at that end of the major axis near the focus occupied by the earth, it is as near the earth as it can be. It is then at *perigee* (from Greek words meaning "about the earth"). When the moon is at the other end of the major axis, on the side of the empty focus, it is as far from the earth as it can be. It is then at *apogee* ("away from the earth"). In between, it is at intermediate distances.

The terms "perigee" and "apogee" are also used for the ellipses in which artificial satellites move about the earth. Usually the distances of these artificial satellites are given in terms of the number of miles they are above the surface of the Earth. For instance, the closest approach of Sputnik I, (the first satellite ever to be launched) in its original orbit, was 142 miles above the surface of the earth. That was its perigee. At its apogee, it was 588 miles from the surface.

Actually, though, distances between heavenly bodies should always be calculated from center to center. Thus, when I say that the moon at perigee is 221,463 miles from the earth, I mean center to center. The distance from the moon's center to its surface is, however, 1,080 miles, while the distance from the earth's center to its surface is 3,950 miles. Subtract those distances and the distance from the earth to the moon at perigee, surface to surface, is 216,433 miles.

If we were to calculate the distance from Sputnik I to earth's center, we would find that at perigee it was 4,092 miles distant, and at apogee 4,538 miles. The ellipse in which Sputnik I moved was so small that the globe of the earth filled most of it. Nevertheless, the center of the earth was at one focus of that small ellipse.

The eccentricity of Sputnik I's ellipse was roughly 0.052. This is just about equal to the eccentricity of the moon's ellipse. Vanguard I travels in a far more eccentric orbit. Its ellipse had an original eccentricity of about 0.19.

Although it is now known that heavenly bodies move in ellipses, the word for the path they follow is still *orbit*. We talk about the moon's orbit, or about sending a satellite into orbit, and yet "orbit" comes from a Latin word meaning "circle." It is a hangover from the days when it was believed that heavenly bodies actually moved in circles.

Once the exact shape of the moon's orbit is known, together with its average distance from the earth, it is easy to calculate the length of its orbit. It turns out that in making one complete turn about the earth, the moon travels a distance of just a trifle under 1,500,000 miles.

It does this in just about 27 1/3 days. To cover this vast

The Moon's Orbit

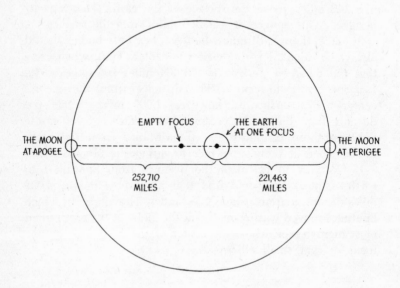

distance, it must travel at the average rate of 2,287 miles an hour, or about 0.63 miles a second.

You wouldn't think it to look at our quiet and beautiful moon, would you? Yet while it floats serenely above the clouds, it is shooting around the earth at just about three times the speed of sound. It is only its great distance that makes it seem so motionless.

THE LITTLE CIRCLE

But now another question arises. What about the mass of the moon? How much matter does it contain? We know the moon's volume, but as I explained at the beginning of chapter 3, that doesn't help all by itself. The material composing the moon may be packed into its volume tightly or very loosely.

How can one go about measuring the mass of an object a quarter of a million miles away? The same way as the earth's mass was measured; that is, by measuring the effect of the gravitational attraction of the body we are interested in.

It was Isaac Newton who, in 1683, first suggested that the moon revolved about the earth because it was held in the grip of the earth's gravitational pull. The size of this gravitational pull depended on the mass of the earth, at least partly.

Well, then, should not the moon also have a gravitational pull? Its mass might be less than the earth's, so the gravitational pull would be less, but it would still be there. And if the moon did have a gravitational pull, should not the earth be revolving about the moon, just as the moon revolves about the earth? The answer is that indeed it does.

According to Newton's theories, two heavenly bodies which are held in the grip of each other's gravitational pull revolve about a certain point in between the two, called the *center of gravity*. This point is on the imaginary line that connects the centers of the two bodies.

If the two revolving bodies are of exactly the same mass, the center of gravity is exactly halfway between the centers of the two bodies. If body A is twice as massive as body B, then the center of gravity is twice as close to the center of body A. If body A is ten times as massive as body B, the center of gravity is ten times as close to the center of body A.

All you need do is find the position of the center of gravity, and you know at once which of the two bodies is more massive and by how much.

(All this is very much like children on a seesaw. If both children are exactly equal in weight, the seesaw can be balanced at the midpoint. If one child is a little heavier, the seesaw should be balanced a little closer to him. If he's much heavier, it should be balanced quite close to him, and so on.)

So somewhere between the earth and the moon, on the imaginary line connecting the center of the moon and the center of the earth, is a center of gravity of the *earth-moon system*. Both the earth and the moon travel about it once every 27 1/3 days, always staying on opposite sides.

But where is the center of gravity? How can its exact position be determined?

This can be done by observing the apparent motion of nearby heavenly bodies that are outside the earth-moon system. For instance, the planet Venus seems to jiggle a little in a monthly movement. There is no reason why it should do this, so it must just be a reflection of the earth's jiggling about the center of gravity. From the size of Venus' apparent motion, the size of the earth's real motion around the center of gravity can be calculated.

It turns out that the center of gravity of the earth-moon system is only 2,950 miles from the center of the earth, on the average. That is just 1,000 miles below the surface of the earth. The center of gravity, although it is not at the center of the earth, is still actually inside the body of the earth.

If the center of gravity of the earth-moon system is 2,950 miles from the center of the earth, it is, on the average, 235,910 miles from the center of the moon. The center of gravity is eighty-one times as close to the earth's center as it is to the moon's center, and therefore the earth must be eighty-one times as massive as the moon. To put it another way, the moon is 1.2 per cent as massive as the earth.

Knowing the earth's mass, which I gave in chapter 3, the moon's mass works out to be 81,000,000,000,000,000,000 tons.

Now that we know the moon's mass and its volume, we can calculate its density. The average density of the moon turns out to be 3.37 gm/cc. The moon, therefore is only about three-fifths as dense as the earth.

This means that we can actually make a decision about the structure of the interior of the moon. It can't possibly

The Center of Gravity

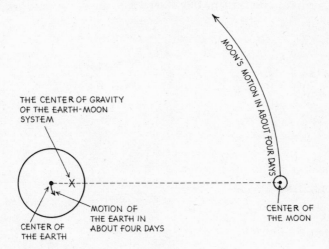

THE CENTER OF GRAVITY OF THE EARTH-MOON SYSTEM

MOON'S MOTION IN ABOUT FOUR DAYS

MOTION OF THE EARTH IN ABOUT FOUR DAYS

CENTER OF THE EARTH

CENTER OF THE MOON

have an iron core of any size. An iron core would make the moon's density come out higher than it is. The moon's density, in fact, is a bit less than the density of earth's mantle, so astronomers suspect that the moon is pure mantle throughout.

Remember that I said the earth's structure was something like an egg, with the iron core resembling the yolk and the mantle resembling the white. Well, to carry on this comparison, the moon is solid white, without any yolk.

There is new evidence in favor of this view. On September 12, 1959, the Soviet Union launched a rocket, *Lunik II*, which actually struck the moon. (It was the first man-made object ever to come to rest on another world.) It sent back information which showed there were no radiation belts about the moon. Apparently this means the moon does not have a magnetic field.

Most scientists think that the earth's magnetic field is produced by the slow currents in its liquid iron core. If the moon has no magnetic field, that must be because it has no liquid iron core. Again this shows it is all white and has no yolk.

EIGHT

WE ARE PULLED

THE RISE AND FALL OF THE OCEAN

You can't very well expect to have two bodies as large as the earth and the moon as close together as they are without having one affect the other.

To be sure, men have always suspected the moon had some effect on us, but usually their guesses were wrong. For thousands of years, for instance, farmers have thought that crops would grow better if planted at a particular phase of the moon.

The phases of the moon were also thought to have something to do with weather. Ghosts and witches were thought to be more active under some phases than others. The full moon was supposed to drive men mad, so that our word "lunatic" for madman comes from "Luna," the Latin word for the moon.

All this, however, is superstition.

Yet the moon does indeed have very real and very powerful effects on the earth. Few men suspected, however, the moon to be responsible for these effects until quite modern times.

Let's see what these effects are.

The moon's gravitational pull is exerted on the earth at all times. The amount of pull depends, partly, upon distance, of course. The surface of the earth, along that portion facing the moon, is closer to the moon than the center of the earth is. That part of the surface gets a stronger pull. On the other hand, the center of the earth is closer to the moon than the surface of the earth on the other side, so the center is pulled more strongly than the distant surface is.

The earth, so to speak, is stretched in the direction of the moon. The solid earth does not stretch much, however (only about nine inches on each side), and only delicate measurements can show this stretch.

The ocean, however, is another matter. Water is not stiff and rigid as the solid land is. Water will heap up. The part of the ocean on the side of the earth just facing the moon is pulled harder than is any other part of the ocean. It therefore heaps up there to a height of about 2½ feet.

The part of the ocean just on the opposite side of the moon is pulled less than any other part of the ocean. The rest of the ocean is pulled away from it, so to speak, and a heap of water 2½ feet high is left behind.

There are thus two heaps of water, one on the side facing the moon, one on the side away from the moon. As the earth rotates, those heaps of water stay in place, toward and away from the moon. To a person on the surface of our planet, however, it is the earth that seems to stand still, while the heaps of water move, each one circling the earth.

The water heaps are not very high, and if the earth were all ocean they would never be noticed. However, the presence of land allows them to show up.

Suppose you were on an island surrounded by vast stretches of ocean on all sides. As the earth turned, this island would eventually run into the heap of water on the side facing the moon. If you were sitting on the seashore you would notice that the water level of the ocean was gradually rising; that the ocean was gradually creeping up the shore. The rise might be only 2½ feet, but if the beach sloped very gently, the ocean might advance many yards up the shore as a result of this rise.

Once the rotating earth passes the crest of the heap, the water level sinks again. The ocean moves out, perhaps many yards when there is a gently sloping sea bottom. Then you are approaching the heap of water on the side of the earth facing away from the moon. Up goes sea level again, then out again, when you have passed that crest.

Twice a day the ocean comes in; twice a day the ocean goes out. These are the *tides*. There is *high tide* at the crest of the heap of water and *low tide* in the trough between the heaps. If the moon were standing still, high tides would come every twelve hours exactly. However, the moon moves in the same direction that the earth is rotating, so it takes a little extra time for the rotating earth to catch up with the moon each time around. Therefore there is a high tide every 12 hours 25 minutes on the average.

You might think that men would certainly notice the connection between the moon and the tides, but it isn't as easy as that. (A Greek explorer, Pytheas of Massilia, did suggest such a connection as long ago at 300 B.C., but no one listened to him.)

To be sure, there is a high tide whenever the moon is high in the sky. On the other hand, every other high tide takes place with the moon nowhere in the sky at all. (Actually, it is shining on the other side of the earth, directly opposite, but early man didn't have that too clearly in mind.)

Another trouble was that sometimes, when the moon was high in the sky, so was the sun. Then the moon's light was drowned out. It isn't easy to make a connection between a high tide and an invisible moon.

The worst of it all, though, is that earth's continents break up the smooth flow of the water heaps and spoil their regularity. As the earth turns so a continent approaches the heap of water, that heap begins to scrape against the shallow bottom of the ocean edges near land. This is a kind of friction which delays the tides. The amount of delay depends on the depth of the sea and the shape of the shoreline. All this makes the tides seem quite irregular and hard to tie in with the regular motion of the moon.

Even the height of the tide depends on the shape of the land. For instance, the Mediterranean Sea is open to the Atlantic Ocean only at the narrow strait at Gibraltar. When the heap of water reaches Gibraltar, it starts pouring into the Mediterranean, but it can only do so slowly because the opening is narrow. By the time just a little has passed through, the earth has rotated to the point where the heap of water is passed. Between the heaps, there isn't time for much water to leave the Mediterranean, either.

The result is that tides in the Mediterranean are quite small, not more than a few inches up and down. This was too bad, in a way. The most active minds of ancient times belonged to the Greeks, but they lived on the Mediterranean and therefore didn't get a chance to study tides properly.

(There are also places where tides are very high. Sometimes a shoreline is shaped like a funnel with the broad end open to the ocean. A large quantity of the heap of waters enters the broad end. As the shoreline narrows, this quantity must heap up higher and higher. The Bay of Fundy, between Nova Scotia and New Brunswick, is the best example. There tides may pile up fifty or sixty feet.)

Then, just to confuse things completely, the sun also causes tides. The sun's tides are only one-third as large as the moon's tides. However, when the sun and the moon are pulling in the same direction (at new moon) or in opposite directions (at full moon), the sun's tides add to the moon's tides and high tide becomes particularly high. These are the *spring tides*. When the sun and the moon pull at right angles, the two effects partly cancel each other and high tide isn't very high. These are the *neap tides,* which come when the moon is in first quarter or last quarter.

Spring tides and neap tides occur alternately, and about a week apart.

As you can see, with all these complications, it isn't easy to notice that it is the moon which is heaping up the waters.

Even the great scientist Galileo thought the tides came about because the oceans sloshed a little (like the coffee in a cup when you're carrying it) as the earth rotated. He denied there could be any connection with the moon.

It was only in 1683 that Isaac Newton gave what we now consider to be the correct explanation. He worked out the theory of gravitation and showed that the pull of the moon (and the sun) on the earth could just account for the tides.

Tides have a tiny effect on the earth's rotation. Earth is surrounded by the vacuum of space and there seems nothing there to interfere with its rotation. It should keep turning forever at a constant speed, and so it does—almost. In 1787, the French astronomer, Pierre S. Laplace, studying the motion of the moon very carefully, decided that certain features of the motion could be best explained by supposing the earth's rotation to be slowing very slightly.

You see, as the earth turns, it keeps moving the surface of the lithosphere through the tidal heap of waters. When the heap passes over shallow seas near the continents, it scrapes against the sea bottom, as I've said. This scraping absorbs some of the energy of rotation and acts just as a brake would act on the wheels of a car. The shallow Bering Sea (between Alaska and Siberia) and the shallow Irish Sea (between England and Ireland) account for much of this effect.

The result of loss of some of the energy of rotation is that the earth's spin is very, very gradually slowing up. It doesn't amount to much. Our day is getting one second longer every thousand years. This is enough, however, for astronomers to notice, as they observe the heavenly bodies.

And the moon, mostly, can be thanked for it.

The Wobbling Axis

There is another peculiarity in earth's behavior that can be explained by the moon. To get to that, however, I must make a little detour.

The axis of the earth (the imaginary line about which the earth rotates) may be pictured as sticking out of the earth until it intersects the sky at both ends. The point at which the north end meets the sky is called the *north celestial pole*. The south ends meets the sky at the *south celestial pole*.

Because of the earth's rotation, the sky seems to us to turn from east to west about this extended axis in twenty-four hours. This apparent motion behaves just as does the motion of the earth's surface—only in reverse.

A particular star on the *celestial equator* (halfway between the celestial poles) moves fastest and makes the largest possible circle. Stars located nearer and nearer the celestial poles make smaller and smaller circles, and the celestial poles themselves do not move at all. (I explained this in connection with the motion of Earth's surface in Chapter 2.)

Near the north celestial pole, only 1 degree 3 minutes away, is a bright star called *Polaris* (also called the "pole star" and the "north star"). It makes a small circle around the north celestial pole, a circle about four times as wide as the circle of the moon. This is such a small circle that to a casual observer Polaris never seems to change position.

Polaris, for that reason, always indicates the north, and is a valuable help in finding directions. In the days before compasses, Polaris was the direction finder. If the night was clear, ships could always tell the direction in which they were heading.

About 130 B.C. the Greek astronomer Hipparchus noticed an odd thing in connection with the sun's motion against the stars.

Twice a year, it seems, the sun crosses the celestial equator and shines directly above the earth's equator. These moments are called the *equinoxes*. Hipparchus compared astronomical records made over hundreds of years, first by Babylonian astronomers, then by Greek astronomers. In doing so he found that the sun slowly changed position against the stars at the time of the equinoxes. Each year the sun crossed the celestial equator at a point a little farther to the east than it had the year before. The east is the direction of morning, so that the time of equinox, as measured by the stars, is a little earlier each time. Each equinox precedes ("goes before") the one before.

For this reason the shift is called the *precession of the equinoxes*. (Babylonian astronomers may have discovered this themselves two hundred years before the time of Hipparchus.)

Hipparchus decided that this shift could be most easily explained by supposing that the position of the north celestial pole was changing. If that were so, the whole sky would seem to shift in a single piece, carrying the stars (but not the sun, moon or planets) with it. Hipparchus calculated that the precession of the equinoxes could be accounted for, if the north celestial pole moved in a complete circle (about 45 degrees in diameter) every 25,800 years.

At the present moment the position of the north celestial pole is shifting toward Polaris. By 2100 A.D. it will be as close to that star as it can be. Polaris will then be only half a degree from the north celestial pole. After that, the north celestial pole will drift away from Polaris. No other bright star will ever be as close to the north celestial pole as Polaris is.

In ancient Egyptian times, about 5,000 years ago, a star called Thuban was the nearest bright star to the north celestial pole. It wasn't as bright as Polaris, however, and it never got quite as close to the pole, being over 3 degrees away at the closest.

About 14,000 A.D., the closest star to the north celestial pole will be Vega, a very bright star, considerably brighter even than Polaris. However, it will only come to within 5 degrees of the pole. So you see, in one way our age is a rather lucky one. We have the best north star there is.

The Greeks had no good explanation of why the whole vault of the sky should shift the way it seemed to be doing. When Copernicus came along, however, he pointed out that such motions of the heavens were only a reflection of the motions of the earth. The heavens didn't shift, it was the earth that did.

As the earth turned, its axis moved in a slow circle. As it moved it kept pointing to different parts of the sky, so that the north celestial pole moved as well.

You can see this sort of thing happening if you spin a child's top or a toy gyroscope. Usually the top leans to one side as it spins; and, as it spins, its axis of rotation moves in a circle. The axis of the earth's rotation behaves in the same way. However, whereas the top or gyroscope completes its axial circle in a few seconds, the much larger earth takes 25,800 years.

Copernicus, however, did not try to explain why the earth's axis behaves so. The explanation was left for Isaac Newton.

Suppose an imaginary flat sheet of superthin substance were drawn through the earth's center and out along the equator on all sides, then out into space forever. Such an absolutely level, superthin sheet is called a *plane*. The plane that cuts across all points of the equator is called the earth's *equatorial plane*.

Now imagine another plane cutting across all points on the moon's orbit. The *plane of the moon's orbit* would also pass through the center of the earth, but in doing so it would meet the earth's equatorial plane at an angle. The size of this angle is about 23 degrees on the average. (It varies slightly from year to year.)

This means that as the moon revolves about the earth, it sometimes moves to the north of the equator and sometimes to the south.

If the earth were an exact sphere, this would not matter.

The Procession of the Equinoxes

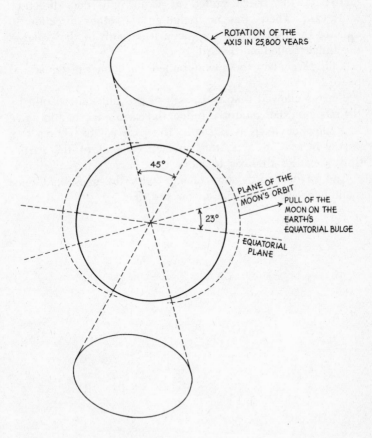

ROTATION OF THE AXIS IN 25,800 YEARS

45°

PLANE OF THE MOON'S ORBIT

23°

PULL OF THE MOON ON THE EARTH'S EQUATORIAL BULGE

EQUATORIAL PLANE

Wherever the moon was, different parts of the earth would attract it in slightly different directions, but these would all average out. It would seem as though the earth were doing all its pulling from only one point, its center. (It took Newton eighteen years to prove this and he had to invent a whole new branch of mathematics, called calculus, to do it.)

However, the earth is not a perfect sphere, as Newton himself was the first to suggest. There was an equatorial bulge. When the moon was north of the equator, the extra matter in the bulge pulled at it in only one direction, southward. There was no bulge in the other direction to balance the pull. When the moon was south of the equator, the bulge pulled northward.

And, of course, the moon pulled back on the equatorial bulge.

Newton showed that as a result of this unbalanced pull by the moon on the equatorial bulge, the earth's axis had to move in a slow circle as it did. (In the case of the child's top, which is leaning over, the unbalanced pull of the earth's gravity causes the axis to move in a circle.)

And so our north stars change with the ages; and once again we can thank the moon for that.

NINE

WE PULL BACK

THE FROZEN TIDE

You must not think that all this pulling is one-sided. The moon pulls at the earth and produces interesting effects, to be sure. However, the earth pulls at the moon also.

In fact, the earth's pull on the moon is eighty-one times as strong as the moon's pull on us, because the earth is that much more massive than the moon. Therefore, the earth's pull has startling effects on our moon.

For instance, the earth produces tides in the moon, just as the moon produces tides in the earth. The moon has no oceans (I'll get back to that later) but it suffers tides in its solid structure.

These tides produce frictions, just as the tides on the earth do, and slow up the moon's rotation. What's more, the moon's rotation is slowed up much more drastically than the earth's is.

For one thing, the tides cause by the earth are larger and produce more friction. For another, the moon is smaller and is therefore easier to slow down.

If you try to stop the small wheel of a tricycle after you've started it spinning, you will find that it is an easy thing to do. A large bicycle wheel which is spinning is harder to stop. A really massive wheel set to spinning is very hard to slow down, or, for that matter, to speed up. These massive spinning wheels are called "flywheels" and are useful in industry, because they are so hard to slow down or speed up that they keep a steady motion. This steadiness can be used to make machinery move steadily even when the power supply is a little uneven.

Well, earth is a larger and more massive "flywheel" than the moon is. When a brake is applied to each one, the moon slows down more quickly.

In fact, during the many hundreds of millions of years in which the earth and the moon have been circling each other and pulling at each other, the moon's rotation has been slowed to a crawl. The moon rotates on its axis once every 27 days 7 hours 43 minutes and 11.5 seconds. (That's one rotation every four weeks!)

That is a crawl, indeed. A point on the earth's equator, as I said in Chapter 2, moves 1,037 miles per hour as the earth rotates. The moon's equator is little more than a quarter the size of the earth's, being only 6,785 miles in circumference. A spot on the moon's equator takes four weeks to travel that shorter distance and is moving at the rate of only 10½ miles an hour. The moon's rotation has been slowed, you see, to the point where it is turning only 1/100 as rapidly as the earth is. (As a result, the moon is almost a perfect sphere, with no flattening at the poles and no equatorial bulge to speak of.)

Perhaps you have noticed something familiar about the period of the moon's rotation. It is exactly equal to the length of the sidereal month, which is the time it takes for the moon to revolve about the earth.

Does it seem odd to you that the time it takes for the moon to rotate on its axis, and the time it takes for it to revolve about the earth, are exactly the same, even to the fraction of a second? Both periods are 27 days 7 hours 43 minutes and 11.5 seconds long.

However, this is no coincidence at all. It is the effect of

tides. Under the present situation of exactly equal rotation and revolution, when the moon makes one complete turn about the earth, it also makes one complete turn about its axis. The side of the moon that faced the earth at the beginning of the revolution is facing it again at the end of the revolution.

Furthermore, when the moon has made half a turn about the earth, it has made half a turn about its axis. When it makes a quarter of a turn (or three-quarters) about the earth, it has made a quarter of a complete turn (or three-quarters) about its axis.

The two turns match, so that the same side of the moon always faces the earth.

This is not easy to understand. Perhaps you might try an experiment with a friend. Move around him in a circle, without rotating (always facing a particular building or a particular part of the horizon). You will see that sometimes your face will be toward him, sometimes your side, sometimes your back. Now move about him and at the same time turn on your own axis. Turn quarter way when you've circled him quarter way. Turn halfway when you've circled him halfway, and so on. You will now find that your face is always toward him.

With a particular side of the moon always facing us, the heap of material pulled up by the earth out of the moon's solid surface is "frozen" into place. The "moon-tide" is about a thousand feet high on the side of the moon exactly opposite us.

If the moon rotated at a faster rate than it does, the tide would move from east to west around the moon and cause friction, and slow the period of rotation. If the moon rotated at a slower rate than it does, the tides would move from west to east around the moon and cause friction. That wouldn't speed up the rotation, but it would force the moon farther from the earth so as to slow up the period of revolution.

In either case, the end is that the period of rotation and revolution are exactly the same. When that happens, the tide is motionless and there is no friction. That is how it is now.

Matters won't stay as they are, though. I said in the previous chapter that the earth's rotation is slowing down one second per thousand years. The energy the earth loses in

The Rotation of the Moon

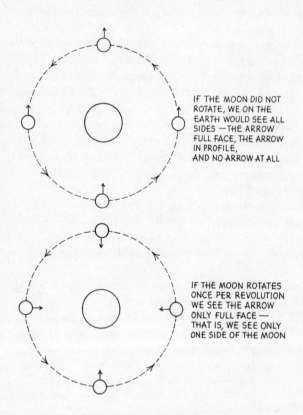

IF THE MOON DID NOT ROTATE, WE ON THE EARTH WOULD SEE ALL SIDES — THE ARROW FULL FACE, THE ARROW IN PROFILE, AND NO ARROW AT ALL

IF THE MOON ROTATES ONCE PER REVOLUTION WE SEE THE ARROW ONLY FULL FACE — THAT IS, WE SEE ONLY ONE SIDE OF THE MOON

this way, thanks to the tides, is gained by the moon. (No energy is ever truly lost altogether. When it is lost in one place, it is always gained in another.)

The energy gained by the moon forces it farther from the earth, so that its orbit grows larger and it takes a longer time for a revolution. The moon's rotation will have to slow so that it will stay the same period as the revolution.

Eventually, hundreds of millions of years from now, the earth's rotation will have slowed to the point where it is only facing one side to the moon. By that time the moon will have retreated quite a bit. Its time of revolution will have increased to nearly two months. So will its time of rotation, and so will our time of rotation.

After that, the tides caused by the sun will continue to alter the situation and will cause the earth and moon to approach again. Some astronomers have even speculated that the moon will eventually come so close that the earth's pull will create tides strong enough to tear our satellite apart. The small particles that would be left would form a splendid ring about the earth.

But that is the so-far-distant future that I'll leave it and return to the present.

The One-Sided World

Since the moon always keeps one face to the earth, that one face is the only part of the moon men have ever seen. This leaves the mysterious "other side of the moon" to pique our curiosity. Men have now satisfied that curiosity, at least partly.

On October 4, 1959, the Soviet Union sent a rocket named *Lunik III* into a path that carried it around and behind the moon. While behind the moon, on October 7, a camera took a photograph of the hidden side, most of which was then bathed in sunlight.

When Lunik III neared the earth again, its radio pulses sent back the details of the photograph. A rather fuzzy picture of the moon's hidden surface showed it for the first time to the people of the world.

Actually, though, even without the help of a rocket, we can see more than just fifty per cent of the moon's surface. I will explain why this should be.

The moon's rotation is exactly steady, as rotation always is. A point on the moon's equator moves about the axis at a steady 10½ miles an hour. Any change in the rotational speed is very slow (like the earth's slowing at the rate of a second every thousand years).

However, the moon's revolution about the earth is not steady. It is constantly changing over short periods of time; and changing considerably, too. When the moon is in the perigee half of its orbit, it is nearer the earth than when it is in the apogee half. When the moon is nearer the earth, the gravitational pull of the earth is stronger, and the moon is whipped along more rapidly in its orbit. When the moon is farther from the earth, it moves more slowly.

To be sure, the average velocity of the moon in its travels about the earth is 2,287 miles an hour, as I've said earlier. At perigee, however, the speed is up to about 2,470 miles an hour. At apogee, it is down to about 2,160 miles an hour.

Now during the perigee half of the moon's orbit, when it is racing along a little faster than usual, it is a bit too fast for the moon's rotation. The moon doesn't quite turn its face quickly enough to keep up, so that it is possible to look around its eastern edge a small way.

Then, during the apogee half, the moon is lagging in its revolution. It is then rotating a trifle more than enough to keep the same side facing us. By turning too much it makes it possible for us to see a bit beyond the western edge of the moon.

Of course, by the end of the revolution, it all comes out exactly even. In the long run, month by month (but not day by day) the moon's rotation and revolution keep right in step.

To the early astronomers watching the moon, it seemed as though the moon were swaying slightly from side to side. For two weeks it would twist slightly to the east, then for two weeks slightly to the west. Back and forth! Back and forth! It reminded the astronomers of the two pans of a scale, swaying back and forth. For that reason they called this motion *libration,* from a Latin word meaning "scale." (Galileo was the first to notice this for he was the first to look at the moon with a telescope.)

It is also possible for us here on the earth to see a little beyond the moon's south pole during half of its revolution and past the moon's north pole during the other half. This is partly because the moon's axis is slightly tipped toward us at one end and away from us at the other.

Altogether, counting all these extra pieces we can see, we can see just about fifty-nine per cent of the moon's surface during the course of its revolution about us. Now what does that surface look like?

THE MOUNTAINS AND SEAS OF THE MOON

When the moon is full it looks like a silvery circle of light, marked by some dimmer patches.

Primitive people, watching the moon, often imagined it to be just what it seemed, a round polished piece of metal, perhaps, gleaming with light. There were all sorts of theories to account for the shadows upon it.

The theory that is most familiar to us of the western world is that the shadows represent a man. The man orginally lived on the earth but committed the sin of gathering sticks on the Sabbath.

When reproached by an angel in disguise and advised to wait for Monday, the sinner answered roughly, "Sunday or Monday is all the same to me."

"Then if you will not observe a Sunday on earth, observe an eternal Monday [Moon-day] in the heavens."

Up the sinner was thrown to the moon, and there he remains, he and his bundle of sticks. Modern people don't believe the fable any longer, but we still speak of "the man in the moon."

(To me, the shadows make the moon look like the head of a very sad woman. I have given up trying to make other people agree with me in this, however.)

The astronomers of Greek times and later were too sophisticated to believe such folk tales. They knew that the moon was a large world in itself, though smaller than the earth. They knew that it reflected light from the sun. Its shape (full, half, crescent, or in-between) depended on the position of the sun with respect to the moon.

A few therefore wondered if the shadows might not be the marks of oceans; if there might not be mountains and rivers and cities on the moon. But there was no way of their ever knowing without a telescope.

Even in ancient days, however, there were writers who decided not to wait for science, but to make some conclusions of their own. They made up fanciful tales about human beings reaching the moon and finding living beings there. The best-known example of such ancient science fiction is a story by a Syrian writer named Lucian of Samosata, published about 125 A.D. It deals with a man who flew to the moon on the back of a giant eagle. (In those days, you see, men assumed that the atmosphere went upward indefinitely.)

By early modern times, however, people began to realize that between the moon and the earth lay many thousands upon thousands of miles of vacuum. The moon could not be reached by birds or balloons or winged horses. (Once Torricelli invented the barometer, it was realized that the atmosphere couldn't possibly extend upward for very many miles, since there was only 14.57 pounds of it over every square inch of the earth's surface.)

This seemed to make trips to the moon hopeless. Just the same, interest in the moon as another world increased sharply once the telescope was invented. In 1609 Galileo turned his first telescope upward, and the first thing he looked at was the moon.

Behold! He saw mountains!

The moon was indeed a world like the earth. (This went against the most famous Greek philosopher of all, Aristotle. He had thought that all things heavenly, including the moon, were perfect. Surely a perfect sphere couldn't have a rough mountainous surface.)

Some of the mountains were ring-shaped, as though they were gigantic volcanic craters. The dark patches on the moon turned out to be level areas that seemed to be without mountains or craters.

Galileo believed that the dark, shadowy areas were seas.

Astronomers after Galileo studied the face of the moon carefully and made maps of it. About 1651 an Italian astronomer named G. B. Riccioli gave the various features of the moon the names that they carry today.

He named the mountain ranges of the moon after ranges on the earth. There are the Alps, the Appennines, the Carpathians, the Caucasus, the Pyrenees, on the moon as well as on the earth. These are all mountain ranges of Europe, of course. Perhaps after the other side of the moon is explored, there will be other mountain ranges to name after the Himalayas, the Rockies and the Andes.

Riccioli also named the craters after the great astronomers of his day and of the past. For instance, large craters were named after the various astronomers I've mentioned in this book. There are the craters of Aristarchus, Copernicus, Eratosthenes, Hipparchus, Kepler and Ptolemaeus. The most spectacular crater of all was named Tycho, after Tycho Brahe, an astronomer who was Kepler's teacher, but whom I have not had reason to mention in this book.

Again, all the biggest and best craters were used up for astronomers of the past. However, the other side of the moon will probably supply proper honors for many of the great astronomers who have lived since Riccioli's time.

Most interesting is the fact that Riccioli was still convinced the dark areas were seas, and he named them that, using the Latin word for "sea," which is "mare." What's more, he named them poetically.

For instance, there is the Mare Undarum, which means the "Sea of Waves." Then there is Mare Humorum (Sea of Moisture), Mare Nubium (Sea of Clouds), Mare Spumans (Sea of Foam). There are also Mare Serenitatis (Sea of Serenity) and Mare Tranquillitatis (Sea of Tranquillity), but to balance that there is Oceanus Procellarum (Ocean of Storms).

All these names are still kept today, and for many years they helped keep alive the notion that the moon was a world as friendly to life as ours was.

In fact, flights to the moon (in imagination) became popular again after the time of Galileo. The astronomer Kepler wrote such a story himself, which, however, was not published till 1634, some years after his death. His trip is pictured as a dream voyage, for he could imagine no practical way to cross the space between the earth and the moon.

Strangely enough, it was a poet and not an astronomer who first stumbled on the solution. In 1657 the French poet, Cyrano de Bergerac (yes, he really lived, nose and all), wrote of a man who reached the moon by using rockets. And rocketry, of course, is the one way we know of in which this can be done.

Usually, such imaginary moon trips were pictured as ending by finding intelligent life on the moon. But, alas, all such early imaginings were in vain. It wasn't long after Riccioli's time that astronomers decided the moon was a barren wasteland, after all. It had no air. It had no water. And without air and water, it could have no life as we know it.

The other side of the moon, shown by the photographs sent back by Lunik III, is rather different from the side we see. It seems much more mountainous and has very few "seas." (The largest of those seas, and it isn't very large, is now called "Sea of Moscow.")

Astronomers don't know why there should be more mountains and fewer seas on the hidden side of the moon. In any case, however, it is equally desolate on both sides. Our faithful companion is merely the skeleton, the "bleached bones" of a world.

TEN

AIRLESSNESS

THE MISSING TWILIGHT

Even the earliest observers of the moon through a telescope must have had an uneasy feeling about the moon's atmosphere. The moon's surface, you see, could be seen very sharply. There was never any sign of clouds, even over the "seas."

Furthermore, there were certain other disquieting signs.

Our atmosphere contains dust particles. Any atmosphere must, for the winds can't help but pick up tiny solid particles from the land over which it blows. Winds blowing over ocean pick up tiny droplets of water which evaporate and leave particles of salt behind.

Dust particles in the air scatter light. That is, a certain proportion of the light waves passing through the atmosphere strike dust particles and are reflected in all directions. If this were not so, our earth would be quite different from what we are used to.

You see, there is light of various colors in sunlight. (You can see them in a rainbow.) The colors are red, orange, yellow, green, blue, indigo and violet. All these forms of light are made up of tiny waves of energy. The waves of red light are longest, then orange, then yellow, and so on. The waves of violet light are shortest.

The shorter the *wavelength* of light, the more easily it is scattered by dust. That means that the green-blue-violet half of the light band is scattered to a greater extent than the red-orange-yellow half. It is the scattered green-blue-violet (which, in mixture, seems a bright blue) that gives the color to the daytime sky. The sky itself has no color but the black of space, and you can see that at night. What we call the sky in the day is only our earth's atmosphere shining with scattered light. At sunset or dawn, when sunlight travels through an unusually great thickness of air, even some yellow light is scattered. This makes the sky a little greenish in hue and leaves the sun orange or orange-red in color. The clouds reflect that orange light and, against the green sky, the result is sometimes exceedingly beautiful.

If there were no dust in the air at all, the sky would be a midnight black even with the sun in the sky. The sun would always be a brilliant white, even at sunset.

Furthermore, the atmosphere's dust scatters light into the shadows. When you are in the shade of a tree or a building or a mountain, or when you are indoors, sunlight does not reach you. Why, then, isn't everything black? The answer is that scattered light from the air shines in, so that the shadow isn't completely dark, but only somewhat dim.

If there were no dust in the air, shadows would be deep black and lightless. Stepping into the shade of a building would be stepping into a patch of midnight.

The dust in the air also makes twilight possible. Even after the sun has set, it is still shining in the upper atmosphere above us. This scatters light, and sends some down to us, softening the darkness. As the sun sinks farther and farther below the horizon, its light strikes higher and higher in the atmosphere. Less and less is scattered down to us and, eventually, true night comes. (If there were no dust in the atmosphere, deep night would come down upon us the instant the sun had set.)

If the earth could be seen from space, the boundary between the day side of Earth and the night side would be fuzzy. There would be a grayish intermediate zone which would represent the twilight area.

But what do we see on the moon? The mountains and craters cast shadows and these shadows are all dead black. There is a dividing line between the day side and the night side of the moon, which is called the *terminator*. It is perfectly sharp, and there is no twilight zone.

That seemed to show that the moon could only have a very thin atmosphere. By 1700, most astronomers had about come to that conclusion.

There was another test that could be performed. Every once in a while the moon passes before a star. (The star is then said to be *occulted*, from a Latin word meaning "hidden.") If the moon had an atmosphere, even a thin one, that atmosphere would cover the star before the solid portion of the moon quite reached it. The star would seem to grow dimmer because some of its light would be scattered by the moon's atmosphere. It would change color because the green-blue-violet portion of its light would be scattered more than the rest.

Careful observations were made during the 1700's and no such effects could be seen. As the moon's edge approached the star, nothing at all happened to the star until the edge was upon it. Then the star blinked out in an instant, with no dimming and no color change. When it reappeared on the other side, it reappeared just as suddenly and sharply. It seemed that if the moon had an atmosphere, it would have to be very thin indeed.

Even so, it was difficult to abandon all hope. People, generally, found it exciting to imagine there might be life on the moon and that strange beings might inhabit our companion world. (Just as today it is exciting to think about possible life on Mars.)

In 1835 a new large telescope was set up at the Cape of

Good Hope, and the New York *Sun* ran a series of spoofing articles about what the telescope had observed on the moon. They spoke of cities, buildings, people. They published drawings and went into all sorts of fake details.

To the paper's surprise, thousands of people fell for it completely. There was a great wave of excitement about it, and the New York *Sun*'s circulation went sky high. The stories were quickly exposed as a hoax, however. (One of the exposers was Edgar Allan Poe, who, that same year, wrote a spoofing story of his own in which a man went to the moon by means of a balloon.)

The "moon hoax" was the last gasp of life-on-the-moon theory, because in 1860 a British scientist named Clerk Maxwell proved that the moon could not possibly have any atmosphere to speak of.

The Racing Molecules

Maxwell studied gases and worked out a careful mathematical theory to account for their behavior. All gases, as I said in Chapter 4, are made up of tiny particles called *molecules.* (The molecules are in turn made up of one or more atoms and the atoms are composed of still smaller particles. Right now, though, we need only concern ourselves with molecules.)

These molecules are in constant rapid motion. The actual rate of this motion depends on two things:

First, the temperature. The higher the temperature, the faster the molecules move.

Second, the mass of the molecules. The lower the mass, the faster the molecules move.

The lightest molecules of all are those of hydrogen gas. These hydrogen molecules move at the average speed of 1.6 miles a second at 32 degrees Fahrenheit (the freezing point of water). At 212 degrees Fahrenheit (the boiling point of water), the average speed is higher. It is 1.9 miles a second.

The water molecule, which is nine times as heavy as the hydrogen molecule, moves more slowly. Its average speed is 0.39 miles a second at 32 degrees and 0.45 miles a second at 212 degrees. The molecules of oxygen and nitrogen are heavier still and move more slowly still; 0.29 miles a second at 32 degrees and 0.35 miles a second at 212.

Even these slower speeds are quite high, though. For instance, 0.29 miles a second is equal to a trifle over 1,000 miles an hour, which is well over the speed of sound.

Moreover, these are only average speeds. At 32 degrees, the average oxygen molecule would be traveling 0.29 miles a second, but some would be traveling more slowly and some more rapidly. A very small fraction might be almost motionless and a very small fraction might be racing along at many miles per second.

Maxwell worked out equations which made it possible to tell what per cent of a particular type of molecule at a particular temperature would be going faster than some particular speed.

I'll get back to these racing molecules in a moment, but first let's switch to another subject.

Any object fired straight up into the air slows as it moves upward, because of the steady pull of the earth's gravity. When it reaches a certain height its motion has slowed to nothing. That is the highest it can go. Thereafter it begins to fall back down.

If the object had been fired with greater force, so that it moved more rapidly to begin with, it would have taken a longer time for gravity to slow its speed to zero. The object would have reached a greater height before falling back.

Furthermore, as an object climbs high above the earth, the gravitational pull of earth becomes steadily weaker, since the object moves farther and farther from the center of the earth. This means that if an object is fired at twice the speed it was fired the first time, it would reach more than twice the height. The upper part of its journey is against weaker gravity, so it coasts higher upward.

If an object is fired more and more rapidly, it can eventually

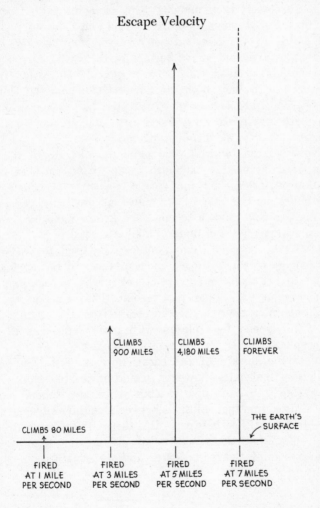

Escape Velocity

CLIMBS
900 MILES

CLIMBS
4,180 MILES

CLIMBS
FOREVER

THE EARTH'S
SURFACE

CLIMBS 80 MILES

FIRED
AT I MILE
PER SECOND

FIRED
AT 3 MILES
PER SECOND

FIRED
AT 5 MILES
PER SECOND

FIRED
AT 7 MILES
PER SECOND

begin to coast very high indeed. Gravity can become only a small fraction of what it is here on the earth's surface. In fact, if an object were fired upward fast enough, it would climb into regions of weakening gravity so quickly that the force of gravity is never enough to bring it completely to a halt. The object keeps moving away from the earth forever.

The speed at which an object can no longer be stopped by the earth's gravity is called the earth's *escape velocity*. It is 6.98 miles a second at the surface of the earth. Any object traveling faster than 6.98 miles a second can escape from the earth. (In 1959, both the Soviet Union and the United States sent up rockets at speeds greater than escape velocity. These rockets broke away from earth and are now circling the sun as tiny independent planets.)

Now we can return to the moving molecules of the atmosphere. Molecules may also escape from earth if their motion is faster than the escape velocity. Of course, no molecules in the atmosphere move at any average speed as high as 6.98 miles a second. The fastest molecules travel at an average speed of under 2 miles a second.

However, Maxwell's equations can be used to tell what percentage of the hydrogen molecules would be moving at much higher than average speeds; at speeds, in fact, that are higher than 6.98 miles per second. That fraction of the hydrogen molecules can indeed escape from the earth, unless they lose speed by collision with other molecules in the atmosphere.

Near the surface of the earth, they do just this. Some hydrogen molecules, however, would invariably work their way, slowly, to the upper reaches of the atmosphere, where the air is so thin that collisions between neighboring molecules are few and far between. Up there, the few hydrogen molecules that do move at speeds greater than escape velocity simply leave the earth and never return.

The rate at which hydrogen is thus lost by the earth can be calculated. If our atmosphere were all hydrogen, it would be lost by the earth in about fifty million years. The earth is much older than that, and any hydrogen we ever had in the atmosphere would have long since left us. Earth has no hydrogen to speak of in its atmosphere today.

The molecules of water, oxygen and nitrogen move more slowly, on the average, than hydrogen molecules do. A smaller fraction of them happen to be moving at speeds greater than the earth's escape velocity. Such a small fraction is lost, in fact, that these gases only escape from earth at an unimaginably slow rate. That is why we still have the atmosphere we do, and why we will keep it for many billions of years.

But what of the moon?

The moon has a mass only 1/81 that of the earth, so its gravitational pull is that much weaker. To be sure, the surface of the moon is closer to the center of the moon than the surface of the earth is to the center of the earth (because the moon is smaller). This decrease in distance strengthens the moon's gravitational force at its surface.

It doesn't strengthen it all the way to that of the earth; however. From the mass and size of the moon, it is easy to use Newton's rules to calculate the *surface gravity* on the moon. It turns out to be just 0.16 that of the earth. A person weighing 180 pounds on the earth would weigh 30 pounds on the moon.

An object fired up from the moon's surface would be fighting a gravity much weaker than it would be fighting on earth. At quite a low speed, the moon's weak gravity would be unable to slow it all the way to zero. In other words, the moon's escape velocity is much lower than the earth's. In fact, it is only 1.50 miles per second.

Even the average hydrogen molecule moves more quickly than this, so the moon could not retain a hydrogen atmosphere for longer than a very short period of time.

Water, oxygen and nitrogen molecules move at speeds less than the escape velocity of the moon, on the average. However, quite a respectable fraction of these molecules move faster than the moon's escape velocity. The moon would therefore lose an atmosphere such as the one the earth has, in not very many million years. Since the moon is much older than this, any atmosphere it may have had to begin with is long since gone.

(The moon may have traces of some very heavy molecules of rare gases like krypton and xenon. These are formed by the radioactive breakdown of certain atoms in its soil. However, it has been calculated that such an atmosphere could not be more than a trillionth as thick as ours.)

Once Maxwell's equations were published in 1860, the question of the moon's atmosphere was settled once and for all. It couldn't have one. It was too small to have one. Also, since the moon could not hold water vapor, any water it might have had would long since have evaporated away. So it had to be waterless, too.

In fact, astronomers before Maxwell's time were pretty certain that the "seas" were not seas after all. Once they were examined with better instruments than those available in the 1600's, they turned out to be dotted with small craters here and there. The "seas" were merely dry and lifeless plains.

There you are. I've already said the moon has no iron core. It also has no hydrosphere or atmosphere. It is pure mantle.

THE DUSTY SURFACE

Is there anything else we can tell about the structure of the moon, even though it is a quarter of a million miles away?

The answer is that some astronomers think we can. There

are certain hints given by the temperature changes on the moon.

There are temperature changes on the earth, for instance, depending on the amount of heat being received from the sun. Thus, it is warmer in the day when the sun is in the sky, than at night when it isn't. It is warmer in the summer, when the sun is high in the sky, than in winter when it is low. It is warmer in the tropics, where the sun is always high in the sky, than near the poles where it is always low in the sky.

But these temperature changes are not really very great. For one thing, the sun only shines (on the average) twelve hours at a time, and it is only hidden twelve hours at a time. Before the day can grow very hot, the sun is sinking. Before the night can grow very cold, the sun is rising.

Then there is the earth's atmosphere, which blows about and carries cold air into warm regions and vice versa. Finally, there is Earth's ocean, which can absorb more heat than dry land can. The oceans absorb heat during the day (or during the summer) keeping neighboring land cooler than land deep in the continent. At night (or during the winter) it gives up this heat, keeping neighboring land warmer than land deep in the continent.

As a result of all this, the earth's temperature is practically never higher than 120 degrees Fahrenheit or lower than 80 degrees below zero. There may be occasional record-breaking days of higher than 120 near the Persian Gulf, or of less than 80 degrees below in Antarctica. On the whole, though, the total spread in earth's temperature is thus about 200 degrees. In most places on earth, the spread at that one particular spot is not more than 100 degrees.

This may seem like a lot, but now consider the moon. The moon is at the same distance from the sun that we are. It gets just as much heat and has the same average temperature that earth has. But it goes farther to each side of the average.

For one thing, the moon rotates only once in about four weeks, as I said in the previous chapter. This means that, as seen from any particular spot on the moon, the sun is in the sky for two weeks at a time and is then hidden for two weeks at a time.

Naturally, the surface has time to heat up quite a bit in two weeks of day and time to cool off quite a bit in two weeks of night. Furthermore, the moon has no atmosphere to circulate the heat and no ocean to store the heat or give it up.

Astronomers can tell just how hot the surface of the moon gets by the amount of heat it gives off. Some of this reaches the earth and can be allowed to fall on delicate instruments called *thermocouples*. In its simplest form, this consists of two strips of different metals soldered together at both ends. If one end is warmer than the other, an electric current is set up in the wires and the strength of this current can be easily measured. The tiny bit of heat radiated down by the moon falls at one end of such a thermocouple and the electric current that results is measured. In this way, the moon's surface temperature can be figured out just as though astronomers had reached up and stuck a thermometer into it.

It turns out that the part of the moon that is receiving the full, direct glare of the sun can reach a temperature of 214 degrees Fahrenheit. This is two degrees above the boiling point of water. On the other hand, the night side of the moon, after a full two weeks' absence of the sun, sinks to a temperature of 243 degrees below zero Fahrenheit.

The temperature spread on the moon is 450 degrees, two and a quarter times the spread on the earth. (Not all parts of the moon's surface reach the boiling point of water. Regions north and south of the moon's equator are not as strongly heated. Other parts are in the shadows of craters.)

The moon is sometimes deprived of its sunlight even in the middle of its day. Every once in a while the earth gets between the sun and the moon, and the moon, within the shadow of the earth, falls into a temporary darkness. This is the lunar eclipse which I mentioned in Chapter 1. The darkness only lasts two hours or so at most. What do you suppose happens to the moon's temperature in that time?

Astronomers were surprised to find that the temperature drops sharply. During one such eclipse, the temperature at a particular point on the moon dropped from 150 degrees above zero to 180 degrees below zero in just a short time.

This could not happen on the earth. Even if sunlight were suddenly eliminated, so that the surface rock began to lose its heat, more heat would leak into it from slightly lower layers. The temperature of the rock would therefore fall only very slowly. On the moon, apparently, the surface rock loses heat rapidly, and very little additional heat reaches it from the lower layers. This could only be if the outer rocks on the moon were *heat insulators*; that is, if they transmitted heat only very slowly. But all rocks transmit heat fairly well, so astronomers decided that the surface rock on the moon must be in a special form—dust.

Dust is made up of tiny rock fragments which would touch each other only at points. Otherwise, they would be separated (on the moon) by tiny bits of vacuum. Heat travels only very slowly through a vacuum, so dust particles separated by a vacuum do act as heat insulators.

For that reason the moon's outermost surface heats up very rapidly under the sun, since it can't get rid of its heat to lower layers. It also cools off very rapidly in the absence of the sun, since it can't get additional heat from lower layers.

Perhaps only a few inches beneath the moon's surface, the temperature isn't bad at all.

There are signs that the "seas," particularly, may be dust covered. In fact, they may be seas after all—seas of dust. In some places it is possible to see dim marks, as though there were craters hidden just under the surface, drowned in dust.

It is easy to figure out an explanation for the presence of the dust. The temperature changes from day to night on the moon (especially the fast temperature changes during a lunar eclipse) put strains on the surface rocks and cause them to crack. (You know how a glass will crack if it is put under the hot-water tap and then under the cold-water tap immediately afterward.) Continued cracking for many millions of years would reduce solid rock to dust.

Besides, the moon must be continually bombarded by meteorites, just as the earth is. What makes this worse for the moon than for the earth is that the moon has no atmosphere to vaporize the meteorites. Every meteorite that plunges toward the moon must strike the surface full force. Such impacts would reduce any rock it hit (and the meteorite itself) to dust.

In fact, the craters of the moon may be the result of large meteorites that once hit the moon. In the absence of an atmosphere, those craters never weathered away. Such craters may have formed on earth, too. In fact, they surely did, for there are actually signs of some, but the action of air and water, and of living things, too, gradually wiped them out.

What we still don't know is exactly how much dust there is on the moon. It might be only a few inches deep, or many feet deep; or it may be shallow in spots and deep in others. There are even theories that the moon is not dust covered but rather lined with many fine cracks. We won't know the full details of its appearance, perhaps, until the day comes that human beings land on the moon.

THE GREAT VIEW

And once human beings stand on the moon, what will the view be like? Complete desolation, of course, and silence. No wind, no sound, no motion, no signs of change.

The sky will be black even though a whitely brilliant sun may be shining down. That sun will rise slowly and take two weeks to move across the sky. Where its beams strike, the ground will be blazing bright; where the beams do not strike, it will be pitch black. Then when it finally sets, night will come on instantly and remain for two weeks.

The stars will be visible even with the sun present (there will be no scattered light to drown them out) provided your eyes are not dazzled by the sun's brightness. At night, the stars will seem brighter than they do on earth, and many dim stars will be seen that are blotted out by the earth's atmosphere. Moreover, the stars will not twinkle, but will shine steadily. (The twinkling of the stars as seen from the earth is caused by air currents in the atmosphere.)

It will be very hot during the day, very cold during the night; our moon explorers will have to be protected from these extremes. A permanent base can be established under the dust layer, perhaps, where the temperature will be even. In the underground shelter the explorers will also be protected from meteorites and from energetic radiation such as short-wave ultraviolet light from the sun and the even more dangerous cosmic rays from space. There will be no atmosphere to vaporize the meteorites or absorb the radiation.

If men must travel across the surface, they will need special space suits that will keep them supplied with air and water, and possibly with food, too. It will have to protect them as much as possible from extreme temperature and from radiation. Meteorites probably will not be much of a danger. The chance of one's hitting a man is rather small.

If the dust layer is thick, the men who go surface exploring will probably have to wear special footgear to keep from sinking into the dust. It will be something like snowshoes, I imagine, to spread their weight.

Of course, these men will weigh far less than they do on the earth. Even with a massive spacesuit, they will probably not weigh more than forty pounds or so. This will help keep them on the surface of the dust.

On the other hand, they will have to get used to handling themselves at such low gravity. To begin with, they will probably be very clumsy about it, and will find themselves losing balance easily. With less weight pulling them down, there will be less friction between their feet and the ground. For that reason the ground will feel slippery.

Moon explorers may even find it necessary to weigh themselves down deliberately with thick metal boots so they can keep firmer footing. In that case, they would certainly need snowshoe arrangements to make their way over dust.

Probably the most beautiful sight in all the panorama of the moon will be that of the earth shining in the sky.

Since the moon always keeps one face to the earth, an explorer standing on that face will always see the earth in the sky. On the "other side" of the moon, the earth will be eternally absent from the sky.

The earth will not always be in exactly the same spot in the sky. Because of the moon's librations, the earth will seem to weave about a bit, moving in a small ellipse in the sky. Generally, this won't be noticeable to casual observation. However, suppose you are standing near a mountain or crater wall, with earth just peeping over the tip. Or suppose you are standing on a spot on the moon where earth is shining just above the horizon. The moon's libration will be enough to cause the earth to dip behind the mountain wall or the horizon, then re-emerge. It will take one month for the earth to make the slow swing.

The earth, as seen from the moon, will have four times the diameter of the moon as seen from the earth. The earth's angular diameter will be just short of two degrees.

The earth will show phases, just as the moon does, but probably the explorers on the moon will be disappointed to find that they can't make out the continents and oceans very clearly. The atmosphere of the earth will obscure them. There will always be clouds, of course, and besides, the atmosphere will scatter the sunlight that hits it and will therefore shine with a bluish light.

The earth will be a bluish-white circle of light with perhaps occasional bits of faint green or rusty brown marking fertile areas or deserts.

The earth will be much brighter to the moon explorers than the moon is to us. It will be almost a hundred times as bright, in fact. For one thing, the earth is larger than the moon and presents more of its brightly shining surface than the moon does. For another, each bit of the earth's surface reflects more light than the moon does. The amount of sunlight reflected by an object in space is called its *albedo*. The moon's surface is made up of powdery, dull-colored material, so its albedo is only about 0.07. That is, only seven per cent of the sunlight striking the moon is reflected.

On the other hand, sunlight striking the earth is reflected at least partly from clouds, which are very good reflectors. (That is why it gets so dark, here on earth, when clouds cover the sky. Most of the sunlight is reflected and never reaches the ground.) The earth's albedo is about 0.30.

Occasionally, as the sun travels across the moon's sky, it may move behind the earth. (Usually, it passes some distance above it or below it.) When this happens, the light on the moon vanishes, and what appears to people on earth is a lunar eclipse. When this happens, the explorers on the moon will be treated to a wonderful sight.

When the sun is hidden behind the earth, its light hits the rim of atmosphere that circles our planet. In passing through that rim, the green-blue-violet light is scattered, but the yellow-orange-red light passes through.

The black circle of the earth would therefore be rimmed by a bright orange halo. The sight of this in the sky against a background of eerily bright stars set in midnight black, and the complete silence of a landscape dimly glowing with orange light, must be more grand and majestic than any of us can possibly imagine.

Perhaps for that very reason, the moon will become a great tourist attraction a hundred years from now. Perhaps men and women in huge shiploads will move back and forth between Earth and moon to see the sights and appreciate the great wonders of the universe.

And outside our double planet are other worlds whirling through space. The nearest of them is never closer than 25,000,000 miles away; ten times as far from us as the moon is. And others are much farther still.

But they beckon to us, and human beings still feel the lure that called men like Columbus and Magellan into the unknown. Somehow, someday, we will reach those other worlds, too.

Since the moon's gravity is much less than the earth's, it will be much easier to blast off from the moon. Conquering the moon will be a giant step toward the conquest of those other worlds.

APPENDICES

SOME FACTS ABOUT THE EARTH

1. GENERAL MEASUREMENTS

Circumference—
  equatorial: 24,897 miles
  polar: 24,860 miles

Diameter—
  equatorial: 7,928 miles
  polar: 7,902 miles

Length of a degree of latitude—
  at the equator: 68.7 miles
  at the poles: 69.5 miles

Height of equatorial bulge: 13 1/6 miles

Surface area—
  total: 197,000,000 square miles
  of ocean: 140,000,000 square miles (70 per cent of total)
  of dry land: 57,000,000 square miles (30 per cent of total)

Lowest point of surface: Dead Sea, 1,286 feet (0.244 miles) below sea level

Highest point of surface: Peak of Mt. Everest, 29,002 feet (5.50 miles) above sea level

Volume: 260,000,000,000 cubic miles

Mass: 6,600,000,000,000,000,000,000 tons

Average over-all density: 5.52 grams per cubic centimeter.

2. LITHOSPHERE

Iron core—

diameter: 3,600 miles
volume: 16 per cent of the volume of the earth
mass: 31 per cent of the mass of the earth
average density: 11 grams per cubic centimeter

Mantle—

thickness: 2,150 miles
volume: 84 per cent of the volume of the earth
mass: 69 per cent of the mass of the earth
average density: 4.5 grams per cubic centimeter

Crust—

thickness: 20 miles average; 40 miles maximum under
mountain ranges; 3 miles minimum under ocean basins
mass: 0.4 per cent of the mass of the earth
average density: 2.8 grams per cubic centimeter

3. HYDROSPHERE

Ocean—

volume: 328,000,000 cubic miles (0.125 per cent of the
volume of the earth)
mass: 1,500,000,000,000,000,000 tons (0.024 per cent of
the mass of the earth)
depth: 2 miles average; up to 7 miles in the Pacific Ocean
near the Philippines

Volume of icecaps: 5,500,000 cubic miles

Volume of fresh water: 120,000 cubic miles

4. ATMOSPHERE

Mass: 5,700,000,000,000,000 tons (0.00009 per cent of the
mass of the earth)

Density at sea level: 0.0013 grams per cubic centimeter

Air pressure—

at sea level: 14.7 pounds per square inch (1 atmosphere)

3½ miles above sea level: 7.4 pounds per square inch (0.5 atmospheres)

5½ miles above sea level: 4.5 pounds per square inch (0.3 atmospheres)

Divisions—

height of troposphere: from sea level to 6-10 miles

height of stratosphere: from 10 to 50 miles

height of ozone layer: 15 miles

height of ionosphere: from 50 to 150 miles

height of Kennelly-Heaviside layer: about 50 miles

height of Appleton layer: About 150 to 200 miles

height of exosphere: from 150 to about 1,000 miles

greatest height of aurora: 680 miles

5. MAGNETISM

Location of north magnetic pole: near the Boothia Peninsula in Canada's far north

Location of south magnetic pole: in Antarctica, near the Ross Sea

Van Allen radiation belts—

height of inner belt: from 1,500 to 3,000 miles

height of outer belt: from 8,000 to 12,000 miles

6. ROTATION

Period: 24 hours relative to the sun; 23 hours 56 minutes, 4 seconds, relative to the stars.

Velocity of a point on the equator, due to rotation: 1,037 miles an hour

7. MISCELLANEOUS

Length of time for a complete precession of the equinoxes:
25,800 years

Escape velocity at the surface: 6.98 miles per second

Albedo: 0.30

SOME FACTS ABOUT THE MOON

1. GENERAL MEASUREMENTS

Circumference: 6,785 miles

Diameter—

real: 2,160 miles

angular:

maximum - 33 minutes 30 seconds

minimum - 29 minutes 21 seconds

average - 31 minutes 5 seconds

Surface area: 14,600,000 square miles (0.075 the surface area of the earth)

Volume: 5,260,000,000 cubic miles (0.020 the volume of the earth)

Mass: 81,000,000,000,000,000,000 tons (0.012 the mass of the earth)

Average density: 3.37 grams per cubic centimeter (0.6 the density of the earth)

2. ORBIT

Total length: 1,500,000 miles

Length of major axis: 475,000 miles

Distance between foci: 26,000 miles
Eccentricity: 0.055
Distance to the earth—
    average (center to center): 238,857 miles
    maximum (center to center): 252,710 miles
    minimum (center to center): 221,463 miles
    minimum (surface to surface): 216,433 miles
Inclination of orbital plane to the earth's equatorial plane:
    23 degrees

3. MOVEMENTS

Period of revolution about the earth (sidereal month):
    27 days 7 hours 43 minutes 11.5 seconds
Orbital velocity—
    average: 2,287 miles an hour (0.63 miles a second)
    maximum (at perigee): 2,470 miles an hour
    minimum (at apogee): 2,160 miles an hour
Period of rotation: 27 days 7 hours 43 minutes 11.5 seconds
Velocity of point on the equator, due to rotation: 10½ miles
    per hour

4. MISCELLANEOUS:

Average position of center of gravity of earth-moon system:
    2,950 miles from the center of the earth (1,000 miles
    below the surface of the earth) and 235,910 miles from
    the center of the moon
Part of surface visible from the earth: 59 per cent
Part of surface never seen from the earth: 41 per cent
Escape velocity: 1.50 miles per second (0.215 the escape
    velocity from the earth)
Surface gravity: 0.16 that of the earth

Surface temperature—
    maximum: 214 degrees Fahrenheit
    minimum: 243 degrees below zero Fahrenheit
Albedo: 0.07

A TABLE OF DATES

("c." means "about")

c. 600 B.C.—Thales of Miletus first studies magnetism.

c. 525 B.C.—Pythagoras of Samos first suggests the earth is a sphere.

c. 350 B.C.—Heraclides Ponticus first suggests the earth is rotating about its axis.

c. 300 B.C.—Pytheas of Massilia suggests moon to be responsible for tides.

c. 230 B.C.—Eratosthenes of Cyrene measures the circumference of the earth quite accurately (25,000 miles).

c. 130 B.C.—Hipparchus of Nicaea discovers precession of the equinoxes.

c. 100 B.C.—Posidonius of Apimea repeats Eratosthenes' measurement and comes out with a low value (18,000 miles).

125 A.D.—Lucian of Samosata writes science fiction story about a trip to the moon.

150 A.D.—Ptolemy's astronomy gives a fairly accurate measurement of the distance from the moon to the earth.

146

c. 1000—Chinese invent the magnetic compass.

1266—Peter Peregrinus first westerner to describe magnetic compass.

1275-1295—Marco Polo travels in China and on his return reports an ocean to its east.

1474—Paolo Toscanelli publishes a map showing the distance between Spain and eastern Asia to be less than 4,000 miles.

1492—Columbus, convinced by Toscanelli's map, sails westward and discovers the Americas.

1497—Vasco da Gama sails around the southern tip of Africa and reaches India.

1519-1522—Ferdinand Magellan expedition circumnavigates the earth for the first time.

1543—Nicholas Copernicus publishes book suggesting that the earth and other planets revolve about the sun. Attributes precession of the equinoxes to the wobbling of the earth's axis.

1581—Galileo Galilei discovers the principle of the pendulum.

1600—William Gilbert publishes book suggesting the earth to be a giant magnet.

1609—Johann Kepler suggests heavenly bodies, including the moon, travel in orbits that are ellipses and not circles.

1609—Galileo Galilei invents telescope and discovers mountains on the moon; later discovers libration of moon.

1633—Galileo Galilei forced to retract publicly his belief that the earth rotates.

1643—Evangelista Torricelli invents barometer and shows the atmosphere has weight.

1650—Otto von Guericke invents the air pump and demonstrates the force of air pressure.

1651—G. B. Riccioli maps the surface of the moon and invents most of the names used for its features today.

1656—Christiaan Huyghens invents the pendulum clock.

1657—Cyrano de Bergerac, in a story, first suggests the use of rockets in traveling to the moon.

1671—Jean Picard makes the first modern and accurate measurement of the earth's circumference.

1671—Isaac Newton suggests the earth is an oblate spheroid, flattened at the poles and with an equatorial bulge.

1673—French expedition in French Guiana discovers pendulum of clock beats more slowly there than in Paris. Isaac Newton explains this by the existence of the equatorial bulge.

1683—Isaac Newton publishes the Law of Universal Gravitation. This explains the motions of the moon, the cause of the tides, and the cause of the precession of the equinoxes.

1735—The degree of latitude is measured in Peru and in Lapland. The earth is finally proved to be an oblate spheroid.

1787—Pièrre S. Laplace finds the tides to be slowing the rotation of the earth.

1798—Henry Cavendish measures the mass and the average density of the earth.

1820—Michael Faraday advances theory of magnetic lines of force.

1833—Great meteor shower over eastern United States. Meteorites begin to be taken seriously by astronomers.

1835—The "Great Moon Hoax" in the New York *Sun*.

1835—Edgar Allan Poe writes story about a trip to the moon.

1851—Jean B. L. Foucault proves the rotation of the earth by the shift in the direction of swing of a pendulum

1869—Clerk Maxwell works out laws governing the movements of gas molecules. Proves moon cannot have either air or water.

1902—Arthur E. Kennelly and Oliver Heaviside discover Kennelly-Heaviside layer in the ionosphere.

1909—A. Mohorovicic, from earthquake data, discovers the Moho discontinuity, separating the crust from the mantle.

1944—Jet stream in upper troposphere discovered.

1957—First artificial satellite (Sputnik I) launched.

1958—Artificial satellite, Vanguard I, proves equatorial bulge of the earth to be slightly asymmetrical.

1958—Artificial satellites, Explorers I and IV, provide data that leads to the discovery of the Van Allen radiation belts.

1958—Project Argus explodes atomic bombs three hundred miles above the surface of the earth to test the Christofilos effect.

1959—Soviet Union and United States fire rockets at velocities faster than the earth's escape velocity. First artificial planets placed in orbit about the sun.

1959—Lunik III circles moon, sending back data on the "other side."

?—First manned expedition lands on the moon.

INDEX

A

Air, 55 ff.
  compression of, 58
Air pressure, 55
  height and, 59
Air pump, 57
Albedo, 135
Alexander VI, 22
Antarctica, 54, 68, 74, 129
Apogee, 93
Appleton, Edward V., 63
Appleton layer, 63
Arc, 36
Aristotle, 16 ff., 117
Arctic Ocean, 54
Artificial satellites, 39, 63,
    72, 93, 98, 113, 119,
    126
Atlantic Ocean, 21
Atmosphere, 55 ff.
  mass of, 56
  radiation and, 61, 62
  temperature of, 60, 61
Atom bomb, 75

Aurora, 63
Aurora Australis, 72
Aurora Borealis, 72
Axis, magnetic, 68
Axis of rotation, 29

B

Barometer, 55
Baseline, 82
Bay of Fundy, 102
Bering Sea, 103
Bible, 26
Boothia peninsula, 68

C

Calculus, 108
Canada, 68
Cavendish, Henry, 43
Celestial equator, 104
Center of gravity, 95
Centrifugal force, 29

Christofilos, Nicholas, 75
Christofilos effect, 75
Circle, 91
  divisions of, 35
Circumference, 19
Claudius Ptolemaeus, 20
Clock, pendulum, 33
Cobalt, 47, 49
Colombo, Cristoforo, 21
Columbus, Christopher, 18,
  21, 67, 68
Compass, magnetic, 66
  variations of, 68
Copernican system, 88
Copernicus, Nicholas, 27, 88,
  90, 106
Cosmic rays, 61, 62
  magnetic field and, 71
Crust, earth's, 50 ff.
Cubic centimeters, 45

D

Da Gama, Vasco, 22
Dates, table of, 146 ff.
Dead Sea, 28
De Bergerac, Cyrano, 118
Declination, magnetic, 68
Degrees of arc, 35
  divisions of, 79
  length of, 38
Del Cano, Juan Sebastian, 23

Density, 44
Diameter, 24
Displacement, parallactic, 82

E

Earth, 13 ff.
  albedo of, 135
  atmosphere of, 55 ff.
  axial shift of, 105
  bulging of, 31 ff.
  changes in motion of,
    111 ff.
  circumference of, 19, 24
  circumnavigation of, 22, 23
  core of, 49, 50
  cosmic ray bombardment
    of, 71
  crust of, 50 ff.
  curvature of, 37 ff.
  density of, 45
  diameter of, 24
  electron bombardment of,
    71
  equatorial diameter of, 38
  escape velocity from, 126
  faults in, 48
  flat, 14
  fresh water of, 54
  gravitational pull of moon
    on, 99 ff.
  highest point on, 28

Earth *(continued)*
  ice of, 54
  lowest point on, 28
  magnetic field of, 70
  magnetic poles of, 68
  mantle of, 50
  mass of, 44
  moon's revolution about, 88
  polar diameter of, 38
  radiation belts around, 74
  rotation of, 25 ff., 29, 34, 35, 103
  shadow of, 16
  shape of, 14 ff.
  spherical, 16, 23
  summary of facts about, 139 ff.
  surface of, 28
  surface area of, 41
  temperature changes on, 129
  view from moon of, 134 ff.
  volume of, 41
  water on, 53
Earth-moon system, 95 ff.
Earthquakes, 48
  vibrations due to, 48, 51
Eccentricity, 91
Eclipse, lunar, 131
  as seen from moon, 135, 136

Electrons, 63, 71
Elizabeth I, 67
Ellipse, 37, 90
Epicenter, 48
Equator, 29
  celestial, 104
Equatorial bulge, 32
  moon's pull on, 108
  size of, 38
  unevenness of, 39
Equatorial diameter, 38
Equatorial plane, 106
Equinox, 105
Eratosthenes, 19
Escape velocity, 126
Exosphere, 63
Explorer I, 72
Explorer IV, 73
Explorer VI, 74

F

Faraday, Michael, 69
Faults, 48
Flywheel, 109, 110
Foci, 91
Force, centrifugal, 29
Foucault, Jean B. L., 26, 34, 35
France, 38
French Guiana, 33
Fresh water, 54

G

Galilei, Galileo, 27
Galileo, 27, 32, 55, 103, 115, 117
Gases, 58
Geocentric system, 88
Gibraltar, 102
Gilbert, William, 67
Grams, 45
Gravitation, 28, 41, 95
    pendulum and, 33
Gravitational constant, 42
Greenland, 54, 74
Guam, 23

H

Heaviside, Oliver, 62
Heliocentric system, 88
Heraclides, 26
High tide, 101
Himalaya Mountains, 28
Hipparchus, 88, 105
Huyghens, Christiaan, 33
Hydrogen, 123, 124
Hydrosphere, 54

I

Ice, 54
India, 21, 22

Ionosphere, 62
Ions, 62
Irish Sea, 103
Iron, 47, 66, 69
Iron core, 49, 50
Iron meteorite, 47
Israel, 28

J

Jefferson, Thomas, 46
Jet stream, 61
Joshua, 26
Jupiter, 32, 78
    moons of, 87

K

Kennelly, Arthur E., 62
Kennelly-Heaviside layer, 62
Kepler, Johann, 90, 118
Krypton, 128

L

Laplace, Pierre S., 103
Lapland, 38
Law of Universal Gravitation, 41
Libration, 115
Light scattering, 120, 121

Lines of force, magnetic, 69
Lithosphere, 53
Los Angeles, 30
Low tide, 101
Lucian, 116
Lunar eclipse, 131, 135, 136
Lunik II, 98
Lunik III, 113, 119

M

Magellan, Ferdinand, 22
Magnesia, 66
Magnet, 66
Magnetic axis, 68
Magnetic dip, 67
Magnetic poles, 67
Magnetic storm, 72
Major axis, 90
Man in the moon, 116
Mantle, 50
  drilling to, 52
Marco Polo, 20
Mars, 78
Mass, 41
Maxwell, Clerk, 123
Mediterranean Sea, 102
Mercury (metal), 45
Mercury (planet), 78
Meridian, 38
Meteorite, 46, 47
Meteors, 46, 47, 62
Metric system, 45

Minutes of arc, 79
Moho, 51, 52
Mohole, 52
Mohorovicic, Andrija, 51
Mohorovicic discontinuity,
  51, 52
Molecules, 58
  motion of, 123
Month, sidereal, 88
Moon, 77 ff.
  albedo of, 135
  apparent size of, 79 ff., 89
  appearance of, 77, 115 ff.
  atmosphere of, 120 ff.
  conditions on, 133 ff.
  craters on, 117
  diameter of, 85
  density of, 97
  distance of, 84, 89, 90
  eclipse of, 16
  escape velocity from, 128
  gravitational pull of, 99 ff.
  libration of, 115
  life on, 123
  mass of, 97
  meteor bombardment of,
  132
  motion of, 78, 88 ff., 94,
    95, 114
  mountains on, 117
  names of features of,
    117 ff.
  orbit of, 92 ff.

Moon (continued)
  other side of, 113, 119
  parallax of, 82
  phases of, 99
  precession of the equi-
    noxes and, 107, 108
  radiation belts and, 98
  revolution of, 88 ff.
  rotation of, 110 ff.
  seas on, 118
  star occultation by, 122
  summary of facts about,
    143 ff.
  surface area of, 85
  surface dust on, 131
  surface gravity of, 127
  temperature variations on,
    130
  tides and, 101
  tides on, 109
  trips to, 116 ff.
  view from, 133 ff.
  volume of, 86
Mount Elbruz, 59
Mount Everest, 28, 59
Murmansk, 30

N

Neap tides, 102
Newton, Isaac, 28, 33, 41,
  95, 103, 106
New York, 30
New York Sun, 123

Nickel, 47, 49
Nitrogen, 124
North celestial pole, 104
Northern Lights, 72
North magnetic pole, 67
North pole, 29
North star, 104 ff.

O

Oblate spheroid, 32
Ocean, 54
  tides in, 100
Oxygen, 124
Ozone, 61
Ozonosphere, 61

P

Pacific Ocean, 23, 53
Parallax, 82
Paris, 33
Pendulum, 32 ff.
Peregrinus, Peter, 66, 69
Perigee, 93
Persian Gulf, 129
Peru, 38
Philip II, 23
Philippine Islands, 23
Pi, 24
Picard, Jean, 23, 37
Pioneer II, 73
Plane, 106

Planets, 78
Poe, Edgar Allan, 123
Polar diameter, 38
Polaris, 104
Pole, celestial, 104
Pole, magnetic, 67
Pole star, 104
Polo, Marco, 20
Portugal, 21
Posidonius, 20
Precession of the equinoxes, 105
Project Argus, 75
Ptolemaic system, 88
Ptolemy, 20, 88
Pythagoras, 16
Pytheas, 101

Q

Quito, 30

R

Radio waves, 62
Riccioli, G. B. 117
Ross Sea, 68

S

Satellites, artificial, 39, 63, 72, 93, 98, 113, 119, 126

Saturn, 32
moons of, 87
motion of, 78
Science fiction, 116, 118, 123
Secondary radiation, 62
Seconds of arc, 79
Seismographs, 48
Shadows, 121
Sidereal month, 88
Sky, 121
of moon, 133
South celestial pole, 104
Southern Lights, 72
South magnetic pole, 67
South pole, 29
South Sea, 23
Sphere, 16
Spring tides, 102
Sputnik I, 93
Stars, 16
in moon's sky, 133
occultation of, 122
Steel, 66
Stony meteorites, 47
Strait of Magellan, 22
Stratosphere, 61
Sun, 102

T

Telescope, 24, 32, 117, 122
Terminator, 122
Thales, 66

Thermocouples, 130
Thuban, 105
Tides, 100
Torricelli, Evangelista, 55
Toscanelli, Paolo, 21
Triangles, 37
Trigonometry, 80
Tropopause, 61
Troposphere, 60
Twilight, 122

Van Allen radiation belts, 74
Vanguard I, 39
    orbital eccentricity of, 94
Variation, magnetic, 68
Vega, 106
Venus, 78, 96
Von Guericke, Otto, 57

W

U

Water, 45
    earth's supply of, 53
    molecular motion of, 124
Ultraviolet radiation, 61
Wavelength, 120

V

X

Vacuum, 57
Van Allen, James A., 73   Xenon, 128